QUESTION TIME

a play by
ROBERTSON DAVIES

Macmillan of Canada
Toronto

ISBN 0-7705-1319-0

This play was commissioned and first produced by the Toronto Arts Productions.

Printed in Canada for
The Macmillan Company of Canada
70 Bond Street, Toronto M5B 1X3

CONTENTS

EVER SINCE I BEGAN to write plays and have them produced on the stage, I have had countless letters from people who had seen or read them, and who asked all sorts of questions. Most of these questions needed, and deserved, substantial answers, and I have written scores of letters to people who were interested in plays, or wanted to write plays themselves. The publishers have asked me to write an introduction to this play, and it seems to me a good time to offer a general answer to the questions that are most often put to me. Some are questions that apply to all my plays: some, to this one alone. This is, in effect, a kind of Playwright's Examination.

Q. *How do you get your ideas for plays, and how can you tell whether an idea should be treated as the foundation for a play or a novel?*

A. If you have a playwright's instinct you know without stopping to think. As a general rule a play has a plot that is more simply dealt with than the plot of a novel. The content of a play is not simple, but it should, in its unfolding, follow a simpler line than the plot of most novels, which may have ramifications and by-concerns that would muddle the action of a play. This is why dramatizations of novels such as *Don Quixote* or *David Copperfield* deal only with a few incidents from the whole work, and often leave us unsatisfied. The totality of a play and the totality of a novel are different in kind.

Q. *Do you make a plan for a play or write it as it comes?*

A. I make a plan. Many playwrights make plans that are longer than the play itself, and write little biographies of the chief characters, so that their psychology may be logical.

Bernard Shaw, on the contrary, said that he found his principal characters, set them talking, and wrote down what they said. Very well if one is Bernard Shaw, but even he was sometimes betrayed by this intuitive method of work. I am a plan-maker, but often I find that when the play is half-written, it gives a jerk and changes my plan itself. Such wilfulness should always be heeded, because it suggests a vitality in the plot that I may have overlooked, or not understood, at the beginning.

Q.   *Do you take characters and situations from life?*

A.   Never. A playwright is a painter, not a photographer.

But inevitably a playwright's experience of life gives him ideas about people, and about the way Destiny works in their lives. Somerset Maugham sometimes worked closely from situations he had observed in life, but he gave them an artistic shape. The patterns that manifest themselves in life are seldom so economical that they can be transferred to the stage without some high-lighting and compression. Life rarely takes the form of comedy, or farce, for long, and the tragedies of life usually take far more time to play themselves out than would be endurable on the stage.

Q.   *How long should a play be?*

A.   Long enough to extend from 8:30 p.m. until 11 p.m.

with one interval during which the audience may visit the washrooms. This is not a smart-alec answer. The human span of attention is limited, and playwrights who stretch it beyond the usual bounds had better be sure they are geniuses. Even if they are geniuses, they may often be tedious. Of course, if you insist on writing an unusually long play, the critics may be so kind as to apply the term "epic" to your piece. But it is a good idea to be sure you know how to be economical before you take a shot at being epic. The noblest Greek tragedies are quite short plays.

Q.   *Do you make money from plays?*

A.   Massive sums. The usual arrangement is that you are

paid a lump sum or a percentage of the gross, whichever is greater. If you write a play that pleases people, the latter is obviously going to be substantial. Amateur performers pay a fixed royalty to your agent, which is the fair way of dealing with them, because their economic structure is different from that of a professional producing company.

Q.   *Do you re-write much?*

A.   Yes. A play must have a shape, and that can only be achieved if you tinker with the length of the scenes, and their placement, and the relative importance of the characters. You have noticed that I always speak of a play-*wright*; the word playwrite, which one sometimes sees, is an illiteracy. A wright is an artificer, a handicraftsman, and anybody who sets to work to write a play should try to be a craftsman or he will almost certainly come to grief. Good luck may enable you to bull through an unplanned play once or twice, but I have written seventeen plays, and hope to write more, and I need the skill of a craftsman to carry me through. Re-writing does not mean that you have lost your way or made a muddle of your play; it means that you are seeking the best way to achieve your goal. Of course you can carry it to a destructive extreme. Henry James wrote many plays that contain splendid plots and fine scenes, but he was never a successful playwright. My guess is that the kind of polish and subtlety he sought in his novels, and achieved magnificently, betrayed him when he wrote his plays. He was indeed a playwright, but he wrought too much. It is quite possible to re-write all the life out of a play, just as it is possible to knead all the life out of a loaf of bread, and it cannot rise. One should stop tinkering just before the play seems perfect.

Q.   *Does the director of the play re-write with you?*

A.   To some extent, but wise directors are cautious about tinkering. They know that their strength lies in their sense of dramatic effect when they work with actors, but that it may be wanting in originality when they work with the text of a play. There are famous instances in which directors played Svengali to the Trilby of a playwright; the association between Tennessee Williams and Elia Kazan is said to have been one of these. But when we look at what Elia Kazan writes by himself, we wonder how much he really inserted himself into the playwright's work. A playwright who knows his job will certainly heed advice from his director, but he will resist anything that suggests domination. A good director will show tact and humility in giving advice to a playright who has passed the beginner stage.

Q. *Do you have much say at rehearsal?*

A. Here the position is reversed. The playwright should refrain from interfering with the director, if the latter clearly knows his job. I make it a rule never to address an actor during rehearsal; if he asks the director a question that I am best fitted to answer the director turns it over to me, and I give my opinion. But a playwright who wants to interfere during rehearsal is a disruptive nuisance. He should make any suggestions he has to the director privately, so that they can weigh their value before trying them out, and perhaps confusing the actors—who are creative artists as well, and must be treated with respect. Too many cooks spoil the broth. Of course, if you think the director is spoiling your play, you must have it out with him privately. Rows at rehearsals belong in movies about the theatre, not in the theatre itself.

Q. *What should I write a play about?*

A. If you don't know, don't write a play. But if you have what it takes to be a playwright, ideas will come to you from the life you lead. You should, however, sift and consider such ideas carefully. At one time I was one of the judges in a yearly literary contest; I read the plays. No year passed without one or two about a sensitive youth who had the soul of an artist, but was not understood by his ignorant and insensitive parents; he either made good and made his parents feel cheap, or he died pathetically and made them feel cheap. These plays were nakedly and embarrassingly autobiographical. They were Revenge plays, and unless you are up to the weight of Eugene O'Neill you had better avoid Revenge plays. In general, also, it is better to avoid the plot about the Sensitive Man (or Woman) who is not understood by a crass Wife (or Husband) but who is too noble to run away with the Understanding Woman (or Man). If this plot obsesses you, get a divorce or shut up. Avoid plots in which somebody, in a situation of stress, emerges as a Christ Symbol, and dies nobly for the rest of the cast. Avoid plays showing how rotten the Rich are, as compared with the majority of mankind, unless you really know something from first-hand experience about the Rich. It is well, at all times, to remember that the Rich go to the theatre, whereas the majority of mankind don't, and that is why there are so many charming, well-constructed, witty plays about the Rich. If you are Bert Brecht, do what you have to do, but it takes something more than the stub of an old cigar to make a Brecht. Avoid plots in which you grossly insult your audience; they may not see that your aim is artistic, and resent you. Avoid plots which have to be floated on a cess-pitful of shit-piss-fuck dialogue; it may appeal to you as realistic, but it is a reality audiences need not pay to ex-perience in the theatre; they weary of it quickly, and begin to wonder what you are really saying. So say what you have to say in your early versions of your play, then put in the dirty words as a great chef would put pepper in a stew; spices support a flavour; they do not provide it. If you want to write tragedy, be sure you have a truly tragic theme. Gloomy plays about large groups of people, suffering under injustice, rarely produce high tragic effect; the great tragedies are about a single tragic fate. The fall of a single mighty oak is more impressive than the destruction of a forest. It is also well to remember that great tragedy is never written except in an age of profound religious feeling—by which I mean not sectarian enthusiasm, but deep concern with the essential problems of life and man's relation to something greater than himself.

Q.   *Is dialogue different in plays and novels?*

A.   Yes. In a novel a whole important scene can be con-fined to a few lines of dialogue assisted by some descrip-tive writing; in a play the dialogue must do it all. Dialogue in a play should be economical; audiences quickly tire of talk that moves too slowly. On the other hand, too much economy may be a mistake, because your dialogue may be-come telegraphic, and the audience will miss something important. A great part of the playwright's art lies in establishing the right tone and pace in his dialogue. It is at the farthest extreme from reporting ordinary speech. Except in special circumstances it should not be too fancy, but in important scenes it may well "soar above a mortal mouth". There is great danger for the playwright in insisting on the inarticulate nature of his characters, for he must make them talk if there is to be any play. But the distinction between fine stage dialogue and the merely manufactured article is a strict one, and as soon as the actors begin to speak at rehearsal falsities and false emphases will reveal themselves and must be corrected. If you are trying it yourself be wary as soon as you find yourself writing lines that begin "Life is like a ..." or "Women never ...", or when you begin to throw in epigrams to suggest a high intellectual tone. Read Ibsen and Chekhov to discover what apparently natural (but artful) dialogue is like: read Wilde and Shaw to see what superbly artificial dialogue is like. Above all, cultivate an ear for what your own best dialogue is like.

Q.   *Do you pay any attention to what critics say?*

A.   Of course; I would be a fool if I didn't. Critics are much abused, and their work is dangerous because they see so many plays under the painful necessity to form and express an opinion in a hurry. Working under these nervously exacerbating conditions they sometimes become testy and hit harder than they would if they had more time to think. Occasionally an ambitious critic assumes the role of Common Scold because severe criticism gains him a greater reputation, in the short term, than more balanced opinions. And, of course, a critic is aware that he, as well as the theatre people, is in the entertainment business, and his readers expect from him a pleasantly readable article and not a careful lecture. But when all this has been said, a critic on a reputable paper does not get his job and hold it by being a fool. Therefore, careful attention should be paid to what he says, and the kind of paper in which he says it. However, a writer who writes with the primary intention of pleasing the critics is in an impossible position, for they rarely agree, and the falsity of his attitude will ruin his work faster than drink, drugs, or women. If a writer believes in himself he must hope that in time the critics will believe in him as well. It may take time, but if he has real ability it will happen. He should be grateful but cautious when he is praised, and patient and silent when he is condemned. What he should fear most is indifference, for if he provokes neither liking nor dislike his work is probably trivial. He should be aware, also, that when all proper deference has been paid to the critic, his own is the harder task, carries the greater risk, and brings the greater reward. Sibelius once remarked that nobody had ever seen a statue of a critic. Statues of playwrights, on the other hand, are seen very frequently, and usually in theatres, where they belong.

Q. *Why are you so scornful of the Beaver in* QUESTION TIME?

A. To make the audience question the suitability of some of its symbols of nationhood. The legend about the Beaver I have used is common in medieval bestiaries; it is not biologically true, but it has a psychological truth. The Beaver is not a noble creature, and other nations choose animal totems that are renowned for bravery, intelligence, and a quality of incalculability. The Beaver is famous only for industry and a certain rodent-like persistence. If I were asked to propose an animal totem for Canada I should choose the Lynx—our Loup-cervier, the *Lynx canadensis*; it is a daring, wily, beautiful animal, swift and potentially ferocious, tenacious in defence of what is its own and never caught asleep. If you insist on moral qualities, it is notably clean and fights only in defence. You can eat a Beaver and many animals do so. There is no record of anyone ever eating a Lynx.

Q. *What do you think your play is about?*

A. It is about the relationship of the Canadian people to their soil, and about the relationship of man to his soul. We neglect both at our peril.

ROBERTSON DAVIES
April 3, 1975

xiii

Commissioned and first produced by Toronto Arts Productions
February 25–March 22, 1975

CAST (*in order of appearance*)

Explorers	Allan Royal
	Jeff Braunstein
Lloyd Robertson	Lloyd Robertson
The Shaman	Stephen Markle
Arnak	Diana Barrington
The Right Honourable Peter Macadam	Kenneth Pogue
La Sorcière des Montagnes de Glace	Domini Blythe
The Minister for External Affairs	Ron Hastings
The Secretary of State	Betty Leighton
Highly Placed Civil Servants	Jeff Braunstein
	Allan Royal
Sarah Macadam	Jennifer Phipps
The Leader of the Opposition	Howard Siegel
Poor What's-His-Name	Martin Doyle
Tim	Lubomir Mykytiuk
Marge	Maja Ardal
President of the Canadian Medical Ass'n.	Guy Bannerman
A Television Interviewer	Sean McCann
Sergeant-at-Arms	Martin Doyle
Clerks of the Commons	Blair Mascall
	Walker Ekins
Commons Pages	Heather Summerhayes
	Deborah Templeton
Arctic Phantasm	Howard Siegel
A Herald	Gerard Parkes
The Beaver	Robert Benson
A Pilot	Guy Bannerman

Directed by Leon Major
Sets and Projections by Murray Laufer
Costumes by Marie Day
Sound Score by Ann Southam
Lighting by Wallace Russell

xv

QUESTION TIME

ACT I

When the play begins we hear, in the darkness, the sound of the Arctic, as we shall hear it at intervals through the whole piece; it is not at all like the conventional wheee-whooo of movie snowscapes, but something truly mysterious, embracing, and alive.

Next, above the music we hear the sound of an aeroplane with engine trouble: it grows worse. There is a final failure. A distant crash. And again the Arctic Sound takes over.

We begin to see where we are. These are Les Montagnes de Glace, obviously so called because of their icy slopes and crevasses, which are shot through with vivid colour and sometimes appear to be transparent. Not a friendly terrain, but one of transporting beauty.

Two figures appear, moving with difficulty over the slopes, for they are carrying a third, wrapped in blankets. At last they reach their bivouac; we can see inside it: a simple, small but not uncomfortable camp. The two men lay the unconscious one on a bed.

FIRST MAN   No use going back for others.

SECOND MAN   Hopeless. They're dead by now.

FIRST MAN   This one doesn't look as if he'd last long.

SECOND MAN   He was alive and he was in one piece. We had to bring him.

FIRST MAN   Why? Consider the danger.

I

SECOND MAN Consider the danger if it were found out we hadn't brought him.

FIRST MAN No rescue plane will come before the bodies and wreckage are deep under snow.

SECOND MAN When they are searching for their own, government investigation can be very thorough.

FIRST MAN Government?

SECOND MAN Haven't you recognized him?

FIRST MAN Should I?

SECOND MAN Yes. His name is Peter Macadam. This man is the Prime Minister of Canada. The loss of that plane is probably known already. The moment radio communication ceased, the alarm would be raised. When the storm drops there will be search planes over these mountains.

FIRST MAN No plane could land here.

SECOND MAN Then they will send in a party from the nearest possible place.

FIRST MAN They'll find us.

SECOND MAN Very likely.

FIRST MAN So what do we do?

SECOND MAN We must make radio contact immediately and say he is here.

FIRST MAN But they'll find us!

SECOND MAN Yes.

FIRST MAN They may kill us!

SECOND MAN If we have him alive they won't harm us.

FIRST MAN Could we say we're Americans? Then they won't mind us snooping around in their Arctic.

SECOND MAN Do we look like Americans?

FIRST MAN What does an American look like? Like anything. We could try it.

SECOND MAN Fantasy! My God, we come here to look for —   and we find a Prime Minister. — Oh well, we

2

aren't the only snoopers here. I'll send a message at once, to Spitzbergen. You get the shaman.

FIRST MAN The shaman?

SECOND MAN Peter Macadam must have the best medical attention available. Do you want to treat him out of our medical kit? I don't. Get the shaman.

[*He turns to a small transmitter and sets to work; the* FIRST MAN *goes out into the storm. Our attention is now directed to a large* TELEVISION SCREEN, *across which strange, distorted letters in garish colours are hopping, gnome-like, apparently in obedience to a foolish little tune of blips and bloops; then a familiar, handsome face appears on the screen.*]

TV HEAD Ottawa announces that the plane bringing Prime Minister Peter Macadam and other members of the special mission to the USSR back from Moscow is missing over Les Montagnes de Glace in the northernmost Arctic.

[*A picture of Arctic mountains, not at all like what we have been seeing, appears behind the Head's head.*]

Radio communication ceased at approximately four o'clock this afternoon, just after the pilot had reported that he was increasing altitude to avoid a heavy storm. The area is little known, even to those familiar with the Arctic. However, a radio message has been re-transmitted from Spitzbergen, reporting that the Prime Minister was rescued from the wreck by two independent explorers. Mr. Macadam is said to be gravely ill, but is receiving the best medical attention available in the area.

[*We return to the bivouac in the Ice Mountains, where the best medical attention is in full shriek. The* SHAMAN *is a terrifying figure, rigged out in skins of Polar Bear and necklaces of bear's teeth; he hops, crouches, and bounds hither and thither, uttering horrible moans and cries; he shakes a rattle and now and then whacks a small drum. Seated patiently near the bed is* ARNAK, *an*

ESKIMO WOMAN. *The two* MEN *cower in corners, and have obviously had more than enough of the hullabaloo. The* SHAMAN *at last stops, and pushes up the bear's head so that we can see his face. He is an Eskimo, but when he speaks it is in a beautifully refined Edinburgh accent.*]

SHAMAN Unfortunately he is not responding as we might wish.

FIRST MAN He hasn't moved. Hasn't blinked an eye.

SECOND MAN The way you've been going on for the past hour ought to have roused him or killed him.

SHAMAN Ignorant! The medicine of the Arctic is best for the Arctic. But if it proves inefficacious we must resort to the white man's magic, foolish as most of it is. Will you have the goodness, please, to hand me my bag.

[ARNAK *proffers a skin pouch of incalculable age and filthiness.*]

No, thank you. My lesser bag.

[ARNAK *hands him a neat black case of the kind carried by doctors on house calls.*]

Now let us see.

[*As he talks, he does the usual diagnostic things.*]

Tongue free and no obstruction in the mouth. Pupil of the eye responds normally to light, but somewhat slowly. Breathing normal and heartbeat firm but slightly fatigued. Temperature; let us see while we do blood pressure. I know all of this already, you understand, but you expect me to go through the routine.

SECOND MAN We must be able to report that everything that can be done here has been done. You know how difficult it will be for us when they come for him.

SHAMAN Yes, yes. This Arctic snooping is a very bad business. What are you looking for, by the way?

FIRST MAN Coal.

4

SECOND MAN Oil.

SHAMAN Absurd. I know what you're after.

FIRST MAN Then why did you ask?

SHAMAN To be obnoxious. Industrial diamonds, you once said. A joke, of course. Well now: temperature normal, or almost. Blood pressure not alarming, but low. No broken limbs, no concussion, no haemorrhages. He's not just the picture of health, but he'll do.

SECOND MAN What's wrong with him? Why doesn't he speak?

SHAMAN He's in shock.

FIRST MAN Can't you bring him round?

SHAMAN No. Shock has to wear off.

FIRST MAN How long?

SHAMAN I cannot possibly say.

SECOND MAN You must do better than that.

SHAMAN Must I? Well, when I was a medical student in Edinburgh, I knew a delightful girl who used to sing a song that had the refrain, "It may be for years and it may be forever." On the other hand, he could come round in an hour or two. Shock's a queer thing. He won't be much trouble. But he won't speak rationally until he's fully recovered.

FIRST MAN What's he doing now?

SHAMAN A fascinating medical problem. My Edinburgh medicine provides no answer, but my Arctic medicine does. He's gone inside himself. When he has finished whatever business he has in there he'll come outside again. Or not, whichever he may decide. I've been trying to talk to him [he gives the rattle a shake] but he's very far in. Perhaps I'll have better luck another time. Just be sure he's kept warm. Arnak will see to all that. Now let me see: one house call, after hours. That will be one jar of caviar. The black, if you please, not the red.

5

[Takes it from the FIRST MAN.]

Thank you. The storm seems to be closing in.

[We are back with the TV screen and the TV HEAD, beside which now appears a handsome portrait of the PM.]

TV HEAD   A heated exchange took place in the House of Commons this afternoon, when the Government was compelled to admit that it has no exact information about the Arctic range over which the Prime Minister's plane was forced down yesterday. The Minister for External Affairs, who is Acting Prime Minister during the absence of the Right Honourable Peter Macadam, said that the best Government information shows Les Montagnes de Glace to be unexplored and unvisited. The nearest inhabitants, wholly Canadians of Eskimo race, are reluctant to speak about the Mountains. Under persistent questioning the Acting Prime Minister admitted that, if Mr. Macadam's plane had indeed been forced down in this area, hopes of its survival must be entertained with caution. No exploratory flights can be undertaken until the storm which at present encloses an area of several hundred square miles has abated. The Leader of the Opposition said that this was a most unhappy consequence of the failure of governments over several years to maintain an adequate ground and aerial surveillance of the Arctic.

[We are in the Mountains again. Their colour is now much more arresting than it has been. The Explorers' bivouac has disappeared. There is no storm, but we hear the Arctic Sound, desolating in its loneliness, and the light on the great slabs of ice is opalescent. Up the slopes we see the PRIME MINISTER climbing, sometimes with difficulty, sometimes with ease. He is searching. He is dressed as a man might be who had composed himself for a long plane flight—a turtleneck sweater, perhaps, slacks, and easy shoes—and the Arctic temperature does not affect him. What is he searching for?

6

Shadows appear on the ice, and he turns to them, but they are not what he wants. A bear appears, half concealed by shadow: he looks at it and it vanishes. At last he gains a height where one of the shadows resolves itself into a reflection of himself, but without a face; very slowly, he extends a hand toward it, but it shrinks away, as their hands are about to touch. He lifts a hand in greeting; the reflection shakes its head. The PRIME MINISTER *turns away, and the reflection of himself disappears. In its place appears a woman,* LA SORCIERE DES MONTAGNES DE GLACE, *whom we shall see again. For the present the* PRIME MINISTER *cannot see her, because she is behind him, but it is her voice he hears. . . . In the scene that follows she acts as an echo of his words, but the intonation of the echo is not identically that of his speech. The spirit of the scene is eerie, and the exchange with the echo is magical, rather than delirious.*]

PM Who was that? I thought I knew him. Was he my guide? I need a guide.

LA SORCIERE Need a guide.

PM Who's that? Who are you?

LA SORCIERE Who are *you*?

PM I am Peter Macadam. Who are you?

LA SORCIERE You.

PM Peter Macadam. Head of State. Apart from the Queen.

LA SORCIERE Apart from the Queen.

PM A purely symbolic figure, you understand—the Queen.

LA SORCIERE Understand the Queen . . . the Queen . . . the Queen . . .

PM It's an echo. But the voice isn't mine.

LA SORCIERE The Queen . . . the Queen . . . the Queen . . . Mine.

PM Yes. Yours!

LA SORCIERE Yours.

PM   How stupid.

LA SORCIERE   Stupid.

PM   Stupid to play like a child with an echo. But it's a sort of fool-companion. And I feel the want of a companion. I wish I were not so much alone.

LA SORCIERE   Not so much alone.

PM   What? What was that?

LA SORCIERE   Not ... alone.

> [*He is disconcerted. The* SHAMAN *has made his way up the slopes, as has* ARNAK, *but she keeps submissively in the background. When the* PM *turns, he finds that he is indeed not alone.*]

SHAMAN   Mr. Macadam, you are on your journeys, I see.

PM   Are you my guide?

SHAMAN   I am. In this place. Your guide.

PM   I haven't travelled as much in the Arctic as I should have liked. This is the Arctic, isn't it?

SHAMAN   Oh, aye. The Arctic, right enough, but not just the Arctic of the geography books, you understand.

PM   No?

SHAMAN   More of a personal Arctic, you might say. Your Terra Incognita.

PM   Where are all the people who came with me?

SHAMAN   All dead. You won't see them again.

PM   Dead? Shocking. I must immediately get in touch with their families.

SHAMAN   You're very nearly dead yourself. What do you think you're doing?

PM   I seem to be wandering.

SHAMAN   Aye. That's what it's commonly called. Wandering.

PM   Wandering, in my wits, you mean?

SHAMAN   You're wandering, right enough, but you're not wandering at random. You're seeking the answer.

PM   The answer to what?

8

SHAMAN To your question. Mr. Macadam: you're in a very bad way; you've fallen out of the sky. Do you understand me? Fallen out of the sky. And you're in the condition that physicians call shock. As the laymen put it, you're wandering. And wander you shall and must until you find your answer.

PM How can I give an answer when nobody has asked a question?

SHAMAN The question's plain. It's this: are you going to live or are you going to die?

PM Die? Even if I took you seriously, the thing's absurd. I haven't finished my life's work; that's important to a great many people.

SHAMAN Is that a reason for not dying?

PM Certainly. Can you think of a better?

SHAMAN You talk as if you had no reality except what exists in the eyes of others. Have you any idea what that amounts to?

PM I am the elected head of a large country. That's what it amounts to.

SHAMAN I wonder how much you understand of what that means. You might find it an educational experience to find out, Mr. Macadam. Very educational and clarifying. Let us see what it amounts to.

[*The* TV HEAD *appears briefly, to say*]

TV HEAD As time passes since the reported loss of the Prime Minister's plane, Ottawa is compelled to respond to the emergency without, however, giving up hope.

[*As* PM *and the* SHAMAN *watch from the upper slopes of the Mountain we see, far below them, and in patches of light, a variety of Ottawa figures. First is the* MINISTER FOR EXTERNAL AFFAIRS, *who is talking to someone we do not see clearly.*]

MINISTER You mustn't think for a moment that I'm giving up hope. Not Hope with a big H, I mean. But we mustn't forget Common Sense, even in a time of great national grief. After all, when he's away I'm the Acting PM. Acting party leader, too. And it's not an easy party to keep in hand. When the cat's away, the mice will play. . . .

[*When the shadowy colleague seems to make his replies, it is the PM, on the Mountain, whom we hear.*]

PM   Look here, is this real?

SHAMAN   Does it seem real?

MINISTER   I don't have to mince words with a friend like you. He's allowed the party to slip badly. The old trouble. I've said it to his face: "You're too much the statesman; not enough the party man." That's a mistake I'm not going to make and it's not too early to start changing a few things. . . .

PM   Can he be as callous as that?

SHAMAN   Surely you should know, Mr. Prime Minister.

PM   But I'm not dead yet.

MINISTER   Yes, yes, I quite realize he may not be dead yet. But what are the chances? Lost in the Arctic. You understand that there's nobody—not another soul in this country—who wants to hear that's he's living and rescued more than I do, but I'm forced to be realistic. Forced to it. God knows, I've never craved power. . . .

PM   This is worse than I thought.

SHAMAN   Don't deceive yourself here. This is precisely what you thought.

MINISTER   But somebody's hand has to be on the tiller all the time, and I happen to be that somebody. . . .

PM   I knew it! I knew it!

SHAMAN   You suspected it, you mean.

MINISTER   Now, let's get down to cases: can I rely on you?

PM   What does the fool think he's doing?

SHAMAN   He's waiting for your answer, in his way. That's what he's doing.

PM   But it's so cold—so inhuman. Am I to believe this? Is what I'm seeing the truth?

SHAMAN   Your own truth, Mr. Macadam.

PM   This is something you've arranged, to kill me.

SHAMAN   It's your own truth. The best of us see life through the spectacles of a temperament, Mr. Macadam, and you've never been accused of wanting temperament. A chilly temperament—almost Arctic, people have said. You're beginning to sink below your surface, Mr. Macadam, and what you see is not false: of course it's coloured by what you deeply are—a chilly man, but not without humour. Look here.

[*He directs the* PM's *attention to another Ottawa scene. This time it is the* SECRETARY OF STATE, *a woman, talking to a youthful, cowed figure.*]

SECRETARY   What do you mean, there's no plan? You know as well as I do that there should be a skeleton plan for the funeral of any Prime Minister lodged with me as Secretary of State, within a week of his taking office. This is Macadam's second term and you tell me there's no plan.

[*The figure to whom she is speaking hands her a folder containing papers.*]

I suppose, in a pinch, we could use somebody's old plan. But who in God's name can this be? "Fly the body to Winnipeg and then proceed by railway cavalcade to Prince Albert, for burial, stopping at every centre of more than 500 population on the route for tributes and wreaths." Are you out of your mind? The last time Macadam was in Prince Albert they threw things at him. You remember that dead cat?

PM   As long as that bitch lives nobody will be allowed to forget the dead cat.

SECRETARY   [*Reads further*] "Mounties with folded flags, two-thirds of which must be the Union Jack, to mount guard at the PM's birthplace until the funeral procession begins. Lining the processional route will be Girl Guides, and Brownies under the supervision of Brown Owls and Tawny Owls." ... Look, my friend, you had better have a full plan for that funeral on my desk this afternoon—unless you want to be transferred to Indian Affairs!

[*She fades, and we are back on the Mountain.*]

PM If they mess things up like this, I'll be compelled to live!

SHAMAN You've said publicly you don't care what happens to your body after death.

PM Tawny Owls! They should have asked me about my wishes.

SHAMAN They did. You said your concern was with life, not death. They leaked that to the press. Very effective.

PM That was in my public capacity.

SHAMAN Have you any other?

PM What do you mean by that?

SHAMAN Have you lost your personal life in your public one?

PM My public life is very demanding.

SHAMAN The inner life has its demands, too. And the reality of death is a matter of the inner world.

[*Now we see a table in the Parliamentary Restaurant. Two HIGHLY PLACED CIVIL SERVANTS are lunching; they are in high spirits.*]

FIRST H P C S I suppose we're looking after the eulogies?

SECOND H P C S Who else? I'm taking care of the one from the Government side.

FIRST H P C S I'm arranging to write the regretful remarks from the Opposition.

SECOND H P C S Much the easier job.

FIRST H P C S I wouldn't say that. Macadam was a shocking egotist; you know it as well as I do.

SECOND H P C S Yes, but one's not obliged to be factual.

FIRST H P C S   "Though we differed on many major matters, my respect for the late Prime Minister never flagged nor failed. . . ."

SECOND H P C S   "Not even when I called him a shabby confidence man and the Speaker made me withdraw the term as offensive."

FIRST H P C S   "This House, yes, and our great nation, mourns a man of probity, who ventured even so far as the Halls of Death in the service of his country. . . ."

SECOND H P C S   Is that for the section in French? The Halls of Death is a bit flowery for English.

FIRST H P C S   You really think so? I'd been counting on getting that in. I want to hear Old Jimmy saying it. You must allow me my bit of rough fun, you know, if I'm to be compelled to write these things.

SECOND H P C S   You can try it if you like, but I'll bet you a dollar Old Jimmy strikes it out. Unless it's in French, of course. Then he won't understand it till after he's said it.

FIRST H P C S   [*In the barbarous French of a politician*]   "Il a ventura jusqu'au les Saloons de Mort . . ."

[*We return to the figures on the Mountain.*]

SHAMAN   You find it depressing.

PM   They were laughing. Little of the inner world there. Not much you could call personal concern.

SHAMAN   The personal concern about your death must be your own. This is part of the price of politics, Mr. Macadam; very soon men are lost in offices.

PM   But there must be personal concern somewhere.

SHAMAN   I observe that you don't speak of the obvious place. What does your wife say?

PM   Wait! Must I see her through what you call the spectacles of my temperament?

SHAMAN   How else can you see anything—or anyone?

[*We see* SARAH, *the Prime Minister's wife, on the telephone.*]

SARAH No, darling; nothing definite yet. Yes, I agree we can't go on hoping much longer. Quite. Quite. No, no; I quite see; in all that dreadful cold and so forth, who *could* be expected to survive. No, I haven't really faced it yet. I don't intend to do that till there's some definite word. Meanwhile I just feel numb.

PM Poor Sarah. I suppose everybody wants her to say something.

SARAH The horrible thing is that there are practicalities that have to be faced. Yes, like when Daddy died. Yes, we all had to think of everything except that he was gone. Right now, for instance, it seems absurd even to mention it, but I haven't a stitch of black. . . . No, not one single, solitary stitch.

PM She's always hated black.

SARAH You see how it is. If I get in touch with any of the shops, or even a dressmaker, it'll be all over Ottawa in an hour. "She's ordered her blacks," they'll say; "she's given up hope." So you see my position, darling, don't you? I mustn't be seen to have given up hope, but when hope's gone I've got to have one decent black outfit, and I'm going to have to have it fast. So I was wondering if I could ask you, as a very special favour, to let me have that simply divine little Yves St. Laurent of yours, until the air clears.

PM That's Sarah! Marvellously organized!

SARAH Oh, that's sweet of you, darling, because, as I've been saying, I've never worn black, and in fact I think it's hideously aging—to me, I mean; not you, darling, because you have that wonderful skin and can wear anything.

PM I know who she's talking to. Horrible woman.

SARAH And, by the way, you don't happen to have a scrap of anything that looks like a veil, do you? The French expect a veil, and do you know, I think they're right. It sort of clinches the thing, if you understand me.

[*She fades, and the* PM *is seen to be laughing.*]

PM Isn't she a wonder? Everything well in hand.

SHAMAN A wonder, you say? If I had to sum it up, I'd call it regret, stopping well this side of desolation.

PM You wouldn't understand her.

SHAMAN Very likely.

PM She's been through this before, poor darling. Her father was a Prime Minister, you know; he was buried with great style. Official funeral—that sort of thing. So you see she's been through this mill before.

SHAMAN Experience is the great teacher, I see. But I'd have thought there was some difference between a husband and even a well-loved father.

PM We've always had a thoroughly modern marriage.

SHAMAN I doubt if I'd understand what that means. Something very different from some old style of marriage?

PM People don't chain themselves together as once they did. We share a life together; I don't try to dominate it. I don't expect her to wall herself up in my tomb, if that's what you're getting at.

SHAMAN No, no. I was just wondering if I missed a depth of affection—on your side as well as hers. But I'm a primitive, as you see, and doubtless I misunderstand.

PM I don't take this dying business seriously, or I'd be more concerned about Sarah.

SHAMAN Man, you'd do well to take it seriously.

PM You're the doctor: you must know how serious my condition is.

SHAMAN I'm the guide, but you're too frivolous to tell me if I'm to guide you to life or death. Yet both are as near to you as the air you breathe. Physically, you're not a promising subject. Is he?

[*He has spoken to* ARNAK, *who shakes her head.*]

PM   What does she know about it?

SHAMAN   She's your nurse.

PM   A watcher, you mean. Surely not a nurse.

SHAMAN   Not just Florence Nightingale, but a very good
nurse all the same—among other things. She has her
eye on you, down there in the shelter.

PM   I'm not in the shelter.

SHAMAN   Oh, yes you are. And you're up here, too. You're
wandering, Mr. Macadam, as I keep telling you.

[*He has gestured to* ARNAK, *who goes submissively.*]

PM   You're not serious?

SHAMAN   I am always serious. Not being serious is a civilized
luxury. You civilized people have large parts of your
lives about which you are never serious. When I had
my chance to embrace civilization, during my student
days in Edinburgh, that was one of the things that
made it seem attractive. But then I began to see that
the price of your frivolity was very high. So I came
back to the Arctic.

PM   And became a witch-doctor.

SHAMAN   So it seems to you.

PM   Is there no price for that?

SHAMAN   We all pay a price for what we have and what we
are. You're a politician. Do you think that worth the
price?

PM   I wouldn't use the word politician, myself.

SHAMAN   Shall I say statesman, then?

PM   Thank you.

SHAMAN   And I'd thank you, Mr. Macadam, to call me a
shaman instead of a witch-doctor. Because that's a very
reductive description of what I am.

PM   I apologize. But why do you choose to be a shaman?

SHAMAN   Two worlds lay before me: the civilized world,

which is so broad and exciting, and has great delights of frivolity for those who accept it; and the primitive world, which is not so broad, but which can carry you very deep down, and is never frivolous about important things.

PM And what do you get out of it?

SHAMAN Fullness of life even at its worst. A union with my fellow-creatures—human and not human—which is sustaining when life is hard. A never-failing sense of the colour and savour of things great and small. I have a great feel of my own skin, and I am always aware of the winds of life upon it. My own life and other people's.

PM You think I have nothing of that?

SHAMAN Who said "nothing"? I have only my intuitions. But tell me what you get out of your life?

PM When you put it like that, it's hard to say.

SHAMAN Can I help you with a question: are you a happy man?

PM Oh, really—Who knows what happiness is?

SHAMAN You've justified some of your most daring legislation by saying that it will increase the happiness of millions. Was that no more than politics?

PM I have no time to wonder about my private happiness. But I sincerely hope it may be said of me that I pushed the public happiness—which is much more easily measured—forward a few hard-won inches.

SHAMAN Why do you hope that?

PM That's what civilization is. It's concern for the public as opposed to the merely private good.

SHAMAN *Merely* private! Oh, Mr. Macadam, what a simpleton you are!

PM No, no; you don't understand.

SHAMAN I understand you want for mankind at large something you don't trouble to get for yourself.

PM I don't know how I could explain it to you.

SHAMAN   Try explaining yourself. What are you?

PM   I'm a creature shaped by democracy. My parents weren't rich, but I was able to go to university, and then I became a lawyer. Law was dull, but of course I'd always had my eye on politics. That was where I found myself.

SHAMAN   And you married a Prime Minister's daughter.

PM   He was a lawyer, too.

SHAMAN   So you married into politics, and now you've got the boss's job.

PM   I thought we weren't going to put one another down.

SHAMAN   Who would I be to put any man down? I've been a cannibal, under necessity. I don't suppose you've eaten any part of a man except his reputation.

PM   I've met you argumentative savages before; you've always got a chip on your shoulder about civilization. You say it's frivolous, but what you really fear is its enormous strength. Conquest by the strong is the rule of history. Politics is the instrument of civilization and the army of the strong.

SHAMAN   Then how do you explain that your army of the strong spends so much time making life better for those who are not strong?

PM   That's something the primitive world never grasped. It's called compassion.

SHAMAN   Havers! So far as I can see, the outcome of your compassion is to make the weak powerful without making them strong, and all they can say to you is Gie, gie, gie! You'll have to do better than that, Mr. Macadam— you or whoever comes after you. Because if we clack on here too long, that fella you think so poorly of in Ottawa is going to stand in your shoes. So let's get on with our job. What's it to be, man? Will you live or will you die?

PM   I'd rather die than go on being bullied about democracy by you. There's no use talking to you; you haven't a modern intelligence.

SHAMAN That's what I decided in Edinburgh. You have one of these fine things, I suppose.

PM Yes, and not a bad example of its kind. I'm not quite such a modest fool as you think. I'm proud of my intelligence.

SHAMAN Ever taken a considering look at it?

PM I live with my intelligence. I live by it. I can't divorce it from myself.

SHAMAN I can. We manage these things with more style in the primitive world. If you'd like a detached look at your Intelligence . . .

[*During the foregoing scene they have not been alone. While the* PM's WIFE *was talking on the telephone we saw, far up the Mountain,* LA SORCIERE *behind one of the transparent faces of ice, gesturing to be recognized; the* PM *did not see her, but the* SHAMAN *did, and gestured to her in reassurance. When the* PM *spoke of the army of civilization, a great* BEAR *was seen, for a moment, prowling the upper slopes. Now, as the* PM *speaks of the* PM's *intelligence,* ARNAK *appears again; her dress is the gay outfit of a Lapp woman; she carries a jester's bauble, with plenty of jingling bells. Her former submissiveness is gone, and her manner is one of extreme, sharply contrasted exuberance; she bounces into the conversation.*]

ARNAK Let's get down to the problem. I know all about the problem. It's live or die, isn't it? That's how it's phrased, anyhow. Well—obviously the decision is to live, but we've got to make it seem that we've considered every possibility, and sometimes very nearly opted for death. That way, everybody will be satisfied. It's important that it should never look like a foregone conclusion. I can take care of all of that. So what are we waiting for?

PM Do you seriously suggest that this is a mirror of my intelligence?

ARNAK What's wrong with me? Surely my job is to see that you get your own way, very carefully giving the impression meanwhile that there is a choice where there is in fact no choice. That's what's called being utterly fair-minded. If it can't be managed by argument, it can sometimes be managed by wit. That's why I carry this thing. Looks funny, doesn't it? But you see there's a knife in this end, and a big lump of lead in the other end. You can use it to knock an opponent cold, or let the wind out of him. Of course, you have to use it carefully, but you soon get the knack. I've provided you with the knack, and we've done very well together, Hero.

PM   Hero?

ARNAK   A man who isn't a hero to his own intelligence is in a pretty bad way. You've always been my Hero, and I love you dearly, and of course I'm going to get you out of this little difficulty in a jiffy.

PM   But I don't know you.

ARNAK   Oh, come off it, you do. You've just never looked at me very carefully. I'm one of your most valued back-room boys—and girls—and just because I'm not seen on the Treasury Bench beside you, don't pretend I'm not there.

PM   I reject you utterly.

ARNAK   You ingrate! The things I've done for you! Where do you suppose that neat idea came from about making mortgage payments deductible from taxable income? Remember the effect it had, when you needed it most? Why, this alone [*she waves the dangerous bauble*] has done a few jobs that put you forever in my debt! Remember—

[*In a spotlight below we see the* LEADER OF THE OPPOSITION, *embarrassed under the attack of the* PM; *the* PM, *suddenly assuming his House of Commons manner, speaks:*]

PM   And there, in the face of what has just been said, sits the Leader of the Opposition, plainly shown to be as complete a jackass as any that grazed with Nebuchad-nezzar.

[*THE LEADER OF THE OPPOSITION's head falls to one side; his eyes close; his tongue hangs out; he is demolished.*]

ARNAK And do you remember what you did to poor what's-his-name—

PM The honourable gentleman has repeatedly called attention to his candour; he protests that he has nothing to hide. No, indeed, Mr. Speaker; he offers us the first example in the political history of this country of full frontal nudity, for he stands before this House shamelessly displaying his engorged ego and his shrivelled principles!

[*The victim of this assault has his clothes stripped from him by means of a clown breakaway, and before the spotlight on him is cut, he stands naked, hiding his privates with an Order Paper.*]

ARNAK The Speaker rebuked you for both those cracks, but they did the job.

PM So that was you. And I thought it was the spur of the moment.

ARNAK That's where I work best—on the spur of the moment—Hero.

PM I don't know whether to thank you or not. That is the sort of remark that gained me my reputation for arrogance.

ARNAK It's part of the price you pay, Hero: the average voter hates it while you're alive, and cherishes it in legends after you're dead.

PM It's stupid to talk about an *average* voter. But you have taught me that my images of other people are not flavoured with vanilla. I dare say what I might think of the Average Voter would be no more unflattering than his idea of me.

SHAMAN But he is concerned about you, all the same. He

and his wife—and some other people that you couldn't just call average, as well.

[*On the lower level we see an ordinary Canadian home, in which* TIM *and* MARGE *are seated before a small* TV *set; on the* TV *screen the* TV HEAD *is speaking; beside him a portrait of the Queen.*]

TV HEAD   Tonight a message from Buckingham Palace has been received in Ottawa by the Governor General. Her Majesty expresses sympathy and concern for the Canadian people in their ordeal of waiting for conclusive news regarding the fate of the Right Honourable Peter Macadam, the Prime Minister, whose plane was forced down in the farthest Arctic four days ago. The message, which was conveyed in both the official languages of the country, breaks precedent because it has never been the royal custom to send condolences until the death of a national figure is a matter of fact. The message confirms the fears which have been entertained from the first news of the plane's disappearance that only the frailest hope may be retained that the Prime Minister is still living.

[TIM *turns down the sound on the* TV.]

TIM   There, y'see? What did I tell ya? They know somethin' we don't know. They got ways of findin' out. He's a goner. I told ya that four days ago.

MARGE   All right. All right. You told me four days ago. But I can wait for it to be official, can't I?

TIM   Well, how official does it hafta get? The Queen, for Chrissakes! She thinks he's dead.

MARGE   She doesn't know everything.

TIM   Did I say she did? Am I some kind of a royalist, or something? But she's got advisers. She don't take a step without advisers. And the advisers think he's dead. What's the matter, you don't think he's dead? Maybe you got advisers.

MARGE   I'm not one to give up hope right off the bat.

TIM   What's got inta you? You gone religious on me, or what?

MARGE   All I said was, I'm not givin' him up till it's official. I voted for him last time, don't forget!

TIM   Am I ever let forget? [*He adopts an extreme caricature of femininity.*] "Oh, he's got this chareesma; I never seen a guy with such a big chareesma!" Chareesma my ass! You know what that guy's got? He's got arrogance, that's what he's got. A great big nasty mouth, that's what he's got. What'd he ever do for the Little Guy? Just tell me that? You voted for him. D'you think that makes him immortal?

MARGE   No, I just think we've still got a system of justice in this country and a guy's not dead till he's been proved dead. And as for doing something for the Little Guy, what about that business about mortgage payments and income tax, whatever it was?

TIM   Came too late. We got our mortgage paid. So you wasted your vote.

MARGE   How many times do I hafta tell ya, you got to vote for somebody that's got a chance to win. That's politics.

TIM   Oh, so now you know what politics is?

MARGE   Politics is the art of the possible.

TIM   Where did you get that, for Chrissakes?

MARGE   At the bowling-alley. Somebody wrote it in lipstick on the mirror in the ladies' can. It's what you call a graffeety. Nobody knows who writes 'em, but they're very big just now and it said in the paper they were the wisdom of the people. . . . And I betcha he's not dead. That's the wisdom of me!

[*TIM turns up the volume again, and we hear*]

TV HEAD   Here is a late report: A further message has been received, relayed from Spitzbergen, about the fate of the Prime Minister and his party. All hope must now be

23

abandoned of the survival of any of the group except the Prime Minister himself. He is in the camp of two unidentified explorers, who report that his condition is worsening, although he is under the care of the only doctor in the district, a Dr. Angatkok, reputed to be a graduate from the University of Edinburgh. Dr. Angatkok's prognosis, incorporated in the message, is, "Wait and see."

MARGE There now! What did I tell you?

[*Our attention is now back on the Mountain slope, with* PM, *the* SHAMAN, *and* ARNAK.]

PM Is that what you actually said? "Wait and see"?

SHAMAN My precise words.

ARNAK What's precise about them? You mean you don't know whether Hero will live or die?

SHAMAN Only he knows that, and he won't make up his mind. So my words have a beautiful scientific exactitude: "Wait and see."

PM But you're a doctor of some sort. Isn't it your duty to save me?

SHAMAN You must save yourself. And it's up to you to decide what saving means. Down at the camp, Arnak and I are doing what we can against your weakness and starvation. Up here we're doing what we can to help you make up your mind, and it's little enough.

PM Up here: down there. It doesn't make sense.

SHAMAN Oh, yes it does. You're wandering, man.

PM Out of my mind?

SHAMAN No. Deeper in.

PM But in a world of fantasies.

SHAMAN Fantasies is one of your dismissive words. Call it the inner world, and fully as real as that other, where you walk so proudly.

PM A world of unreality.

SHAMAN No: a world of another reality. And the farther you

24

explore it, the more significant the fantasies become for the world you think of as reality.

PM So you seriously propose that I, as a man of great responsibilities, should hop to and fro between the world of fact and your world of fantasy?

SHAMAN Why not? Free trade between the world of fantasy and the world of reality is what gives dimension to life. But you're no free-trader, Mr. Macadam. You're a protectionist. You've put a big tariff-wall between the two worlds, and you look for self-sufficiency in your world of reality. It can't be done, man. Not with safety.

PM I have the concerns of a country to think of.

SHAMAN Your country might benefit by some of the free trade I'm talking about.

PM Can a country live on fantasy?

SHAMAN No more than it can live on salt, but without salt what is it?

PM It's not the job of a head of state to dabble in such things.

SHAMAN It's the job of a head of state to be aware of his country. He ought to be able to sense what his people are and what they want and whether they can get it. Or else why is he the head? There was Mackenzie King, now. A queer-like auld wifie, I grant ye, but he could snuff the air on Parliament Hill and tell ye what people were thinking anywhere in the country. He had brains, but he never made a god of his intellect, like you. His strength came from a different place.

PM And where do you suppose that was?

SHAMAN Whiles I've thought it came from his wee doggie. That was a real intuitive wee doggie. Whiles it came from talking with his mother's ghost. Oh, he was a real free-trader of the spirit, Mr. Macadam, however much like an auld wifie he seemed, and when have we had a stronger man?

PM You'll drive me mad, if I'm not mad already. Strength!

I must find my own strength and get out of this mess.

SHAMAN   Indeed you must. And where will you look?

PM   In my intelligence? But you've set up this jester as my intelligence. How does a man look for his strength?

SHAMAN   Have you a totem animal, Mr. Macadam?

PM   What's that?

SHAMAN   A very important creature to many of us who live under your rule, Mr. Macadam—even though most of us aren't voters. It's whatever creature we look to for more of what we need in life than we can summon from our unaided selves. Why do so many of your voters keep pets, do you suppose? To gain some touch of the strength and the wisdom of the animal. But we who live nearer the earth have better totem animals than your doggies and your pussycats. You can't lead our totem animals around on strings, or feed them out of tins. We don't choose them: they choose us.

PM   But what are they for?

SHAMAN   For the ultimate strength. To call on when we need the animal side. I'd forgotten you're a very modern man and a psychological protectionist as well. I wonder could we find your totem animal?

ARNAK   Nothing less than the bear for you, Hero.

PM   A bear would be interesting.

SHAMAN   I misdoubt a bear would be a little beyond you.

PM   If I must have an animal, let it be a bear.

SHAMAN   The bear is a fearsome creature.

PM   Well, I certainly don't intend to settle for Mackenzie King's dog.

SHAMAN   Ah, well: as you won't listen—let it be a bear, then.

[*He takes off the Polar Bear's skin that is part of his ceremonial garb and throws it to the* PM, *who puts it on with* ARNAK'S *help. As he does so, the* GREAT BEAR *appears, mistily, high on the Mountain, and as the* PM *goes through his experience of beardom it watches*

26

*closely, and does with animal perfection what he does
ineptly and, as time passes, in agony. . . . At first the
PM moves very slowly, accustoming himself to the odd-
ity of being a bear. He looks at his paws in wonderment;
his movements are awkward, he stumbles as he moves
on his back legs, and from time to time he tumbles
forward on all fours. We can see his face under the
bear's head; his expression is of incredulity, then the
perplexity of a man losing the power of rational
thought, and finally agony as he is translated into a
wholly alien mode of being; he draws breath with difficulty, which becomes pain, as though every inspiration
were anguish pushing toward the farthest reach of endurance. The GREAT BEAR no longer imitates him; it
rises in might on its back legs and becomes a figure of
devouring menace; its jaws open. The PM opens his
mouth and utters a terrifying animal cry, and falls to
the ground. ARNAK lifts the bearskin from him; the
SHAMAN takes it; the GREAT BEAR vanishes, and ARNAK
holds the PM's head in her lap as he recovers.]*

ARNAK   Poor Hero! Was the bear too much for you?

SHAMAN   It'll be the breathing was too much for him. The
bear has a keen scent, and the whole world of scent is
a horror to a modern man. Well well; it was nobody's
fault but his own. Nevertheless, I'll just be away to the
camp and give his carcass a wee encouraging shot.
There'll be great concern for him down below, though
I don't suppose he'd see it that way.

*[The SHAMAN goes off down the Mountain, leaving the
PM to be nursed by ARNAK, who croons to him as if he
were a child. Our attention now goes to Ottawa, where
the MINISTER FOR EXTERNAL AFFAIRS is in conference with
a prosperous, aggressive, and angry DOCTOR.]*

MINISTER   We understand your concern, Doctor, and I assure
you we appreciate it, but we are doing everything we
can.

DOCTOR It doesn't seem to be very much.

MINISTER While the storm lasts we can do no more. You must understand the Montagnes de Glace are absolutely out of reach by plane or even by a party on foot. We cannot reach the Prime Minister.

DOCTOR But you've got radio contact. The CBC keeps reporting radio messages.

MINISTER Messages from there; we have not established contact from here.

DOCTOR Then you'd better get busy! Do you want Peter Macadam to die?

MINISTER I resent that question, Doctor.

DOCTOR Then do something.

MINISTER Of course I understand your worry—

DOCTOR I don't think you do. If you did, you'd be on the radio at once, asking the vital question.

MINISTER The vital question—?

DOCTOR Yes, the vital question. Is this Doctor Angatkok a properly qualified member of the Canadian Medical Association? Or is he, as I and my colleagues suspect, one of these half-trained Europeans who swarm in here and set up practice without meeting our standards? Angatkok! What kind of a name is that? Sounds Hungarian to me. Who knows what he's up to? Acupuncture with porcupine quills, for anything we know!

MINISTER All the information we have is that he holds his degree from the University of Edinburgh.

DOCTOR What year?

MINISTER How should I know what year?

DOCTOR Aha! You see—you haven't checked. I've checked already enough to know that there is no doctor of that name practising in the Arctic, and no doctor of that name on our medical register. Now we're going to stamp out these European bootleg quacks if I have to go to the Arctic myself—God forbid!

[*We are back on the Mountain, where the* PM *is coming to himself again. The* SHAMAN *rejoins them.*]

ARNAK He's coming round.

SHAMAN Just as well, with what I've pumped into him. He has no knowledge of himself at all, this man. Imagine insisting on a bear!

ARNAK My fault. But it's what his intelligence would insist on.

SHAMAN Yes, but what would he know of the terrible awareness of a bear? No respect for the animal side.

PM Horrible! Horrible! I could hardly see, I couldn't understand what I did see. And everything rushed in on me through my nose. Aaaah!

ARNAK Gently does it, Hero. Now you have your own keen eyes again, and your own beautiful little stupid nose; you're a man again.

SHAMAN A man in his wanderings.

PM I can't wander any more. I'm at the end.

SHAMAN Do you say so? As a doctor I'd say there was a lot of spirit in you yet.

ARNAK And a lot of intelligence and cunning. I'm with you, Hero.

PM I'm lost . . . I'm lost.

SHAMAN Nay, nay, man; you're not lost. Lonely: yes. On unfamiliar ground: yes. But not lost. You're in your Terra Incognita, but it's your own. Take heart.

PM I have no heart left. I decide for death.

ARNAK Hero! You're not going to desert me?

SHAMAN And all that unfinished business? The country you talked about so bravely? Throw all that away because you've had a peep at the starved side of yourself? Where's your courage, man?

PM I have no courage for this.

ARNAK Don't give up so soon, Hero.

PM I must have rest. I want oblivion.

SHAMAN   Dear man, *this* is oblivion. This is your Terra Incognita, Mr. Macadam.

PM   Unknown Land indeed: and I am utterly alone.

ARNAK   You think yourself alone! You ungrateful brute,
Peter! What about me?

PM   It's hard for me to accept the notion that I have a femi-
nine intelligence.

ARNAK   It's part of your charisma.

PM   Charisma! Beloved word of the public relations quacks!

ARNAK   Brings in votes.

PM   I suppose it does.

ARNAK   Women's votes.

PM   At what a cost!

ARNAK   Sex in politics. Very important today.

PM   But it's whorish! I long to be quit of it!

ARNAK   A holiday from the horny?

PM   Yes, a holiday from the horny. It used to be said that
a king was the garlanded and anointed phallus of his
people; nowadays that's expected of Prime Ministers.

ARNAK   And you deliver the goods, Hero.

PM   And I deliver the goods, God help me!

ARNAK   Then what are you complaining about? What do you
want?

PM   I want to be valued for what I am when I am most true
to myself.

ARNAK   Better face it, Hero: politics is a coarse art.

PM   But this eternal cadging for popularity!

SHAMAN   That's the coarse side of democracy. It's not all
theory and persuasion; there's magic and luck and play-
ing to the crowd. Not unlike being a shaman.

PM   Do you have to play this endless sex-game?

SHAMAN   We primitives don't hoach after sex like you civilized folk. We're not always in dread it'll leave us. We
don't think it's a talisman to keep our madness at bay.

30

We don't think it's a shield against death and dissolution.

PM I am no primitive, but I rebel against the sexy image modern bad taste thrusts on a political leader. It is a gross intrusion on a reality—the reality of my marriage, and my feeling for my wife.

SHAMAN You know the reality of that?

PM Who does if I don't?

SHAMAN You know what you see with that Arctic gaze of yours. But I think you do learn, Mr. Macadam—slowly and with pain. If you were to hear her now, do you think you would recognize her feeling for you?

PM Who would know better than I?

SHAMAN She would, if you know how to hear. She has spoken about it publicly, more than once.

PM Under compulsion. The media insist on it. The people want it.

SHAMAN They always want it, and they always get it, even when they have to wait until you're dead.

PM Who cares what the media want?

SHAMAN You care. Let us have no lies here, Mr. Macadam. You care, even though it grieves you that your wife has to suffer.

[*On the* TV *screen we see* SARAH, *the* PM's *wife, becomingly dressed in black—but not unrelieved black—talking to an* INTERVIEWER.]

INTERVIEWER So you haven't given up hope?

SARAH No, and I won't until I have absolute assurance that all hope is gone.

INTERVIEWER How much longer do you think you can go on hoping?

SARAH I have told you; until I know for a certainty that my husband is dead.

INTERVIEWER Yes, but all the reports we have suggest it could be months before anybody can get into the area where he is. We don't even know who these people are that have him. The Canadian Medical Association denies any knowledge of this Dr. Angatkok. Your husband is in coma; he hasn't eaten. How long do you think he can hold out?

SARAH He is a man of great determination.

INTERVIEWER But you have faced the fact that the chances are very poor.

SARAH I have faced all sorts of dreadful things.

INTERVIEWER Do you think you'd know if he died?

SARAH I don't understand.

INTERVIEWER Do you think you'd get a message? Or feel anything? It's always been said that you and he were so close.

SARAH Yes, but we weren't Siamese twins, you know. He didn't sneeze if I sniffed pepper. We had lives of our own. And we are neither of us in the least mystical.

INTERVIEWER Are you religious?

SARAH I don't think so.

INTERVIEWER You don't know?

SARAH Why do you ask?

INTERVIEWER A proposal has been made that the Government should name next Sunday as a National Day of Prayer for the recovery of the Prime Minister. What do you think about that?

SARAH But why name a special day?

INTERVIEWER When your father was dying a Day of Prayer was named.

SARAH That was many years ago.

INTERVIEWER You think times have changed?

SARAH I think anybody who considers it worth while to pray for my husband's rescue is doing so already.

INTERVIEWER Who considers it worth while—?

SARAH You know what I mean. Some do and some don't.

INTERVIEWER And you don't?

SARAH What am I supposed to say to that?

INTERVIEWER   Religion is a very live topic these days. What somebody like yourself thinks about it is of widespread interest.

SARAH   Doesn't anybody think that my views on religion are my own business?

INTERVIEWER   But you understand—

SARAH   No, I don't understand. I very well remember the Day of Prayer when my father lay dying—and he did die, you know, the day afterwards—and I remember how oppressed his whole family were by the thought that an official, organized drive was going on to change what was quite clearly the course of nature. We thought it was silly and intrusive and well—awful.

PM   [*On the Mountain*]   He's pushed her into saying things she shouldn't say.

ARNAK   It's his trade, Hero. That's how he gets his living.

INTERVIEWER   So we may take it that you don't approve of a Day of Prayer.

SARAH   You may take it that I think more goodwill and decency and understanding of public figures while they are living would be better than official prayers when they are—perhaps—dying or already dead.

[*She is angry and hurt, and maintains her composure with difficulty, as the* INTERVIEWER *moves in for the kill.*]

INTERVIEWER   You know that your own public image has always been a very cool one. People will be glad to know that—

SARAH   That when my husband is lost, and may be in terrible straits, or already dead, I can feel emotion just like those poor women you show weeping when their children have been lost in fires.

INTERVIEWER   I'm sure our many thousands of viewers feel for you deeply.

SARAH   But they'd feel even more deeply if I broke down and cried, wouldn't they?

33

INTERVIEWER I'm sure nobody wants that.

SARAH Don't they? Wouldn't it be a triumph for you? What is it they say? "The medium is the massacre"?

INTERVIEWER I'm sure nobody wants to cause you distress.

SARAH But they would welcome some assurance that I really am in distress.

INTERVIEWER I didn't say that.

SARAH Of course not. That is the essence of your squalid art; getting across what you mean without saying it; making somebody else say more than they had any intention of saying. Well, I'm a public figure, as you say, and I'll play the game. I assure anybody who may be watching us that I am more wretched now than I ever thought it possible to be. I'm trying to be honest, and I'm trying to be true to myself, and of course I'm trying to do what my husband would expect. So if I'm not a very satisfactory public figure, please try to forgive me.

INTERVIEWER [*Wrapping up the interview*] I am sure all of us sympathize deeply with our guest tonight, Mrs. Peter Macadam, in what must now be considered the loss of a great public figure—

SARAH [*Intervening*] I have not lost a public figure! Nobody knows what I have lost!

[*Though under great strain she does not break down, and is not in the least hysterical; she and the* INTERVIEWER *disappear.*

Now we are back on the Mountain, with the PM, *the* SHAMAN, *and* ARNAK.]

SHAMAN Your wife spoke well, Mr. Macadam, didn't you think?

PM Yes—yes, certainly.

ARNAK Come on, Hero; you have doubts, haven't you? You wish she hadn't used that word "squalid".

PM It may have been unwise.

ARNAK Damn right it was unwise. Very thin skins in the

34

media. I can see the comments: "PM's Wife Waits Without Hope and Without Faith"; "WASP Wife Keeps Stiff Upper Lip". They'll know just where to put the knife in.

PM She did wonderfully well. She has style.

ARNAK You can pay too much for style. It tells you what's squalid when it's more tactful not to know.

PM I once thought I had style, but I learned when it was wiser to be dull.

ARNAK Not so bad as that, Hero; you exchanged style for charisma. Charisma embraces; style excludes.

PM Oh, but to be one's best self, without thinking about embracing or excluding! To do what one knows to be right without having to persuade every good, dull supporter and provide an answer for every dull, envious detractor.

SHAMAN To love one's wife without reservations or criticisms!

PM What did you say?

SHAMAN I said what you are thinking, Mr. Macadam. You are wondering how much that unfortunate word "squalid" might cost you.

PM She is herself. Surely she can say what she likes?

SHAMAN She can say what she likes, but you must foot the bill. Isn't that the way of it?

PM Suppose I admit that things between Sarah and me haven't always been smooth? Surely it's a private matter?

SHAMAN In important things there is no public or private. The flaw within becomes the flaw without, because public matters are the mirrors in which we see private matters. You'd have done better to get things straight with your wife many a long day ago.

PM Everything's as straight as it ever will be.

SHAMAN How straight is that?

[SARAH *has joined them on the Mountain; she is in the* *mourning clothes she wore during the* TV *interview.*]

35

PM   Always this impertinent interrogation? Who are you to plague me like this? Why don't you let me alone?

SHAMAN   We are fantasies, Mr. Macadam. We cannot be banished.

PM   If you are my fantasies—creatures of my imagination—why are you so remorselessly contentious?

SHAMAN   Ah, Mr. Macadam, only a stranger to his inner world could ask such a question.

PM   I say you are not fantasies. I saw my wife just now, as clearly and as much herself as I have ever seen her.

SHAMAN   Ah, what you see down there, Mr. Macadam, is real enough. But what you see on the Mountain is both insubstantial and truer than reality. If we speak in doubts, they are your own doubts.

PM   Always so critical! Forever judging! You call yourselves fantasies but you are as rough as nightmares. Nobody stands with me.

SARAH   Don't say that, Peter.

PM   Sarah!

SARAH   I've stood with you so long that now there's no place else for me to be.

PM   And you've always spoken as my best self!

SARAH   Oh, my dear, don't say that. You've said it often, and it's a very pretty speech, but we both know better, don't we?

PM   You have always been closest to my heart.

SARAH   Not always, Peter, but sometimes.

PM   I have always turned to you—

SARAH   When you were tired, or beaten, or didn't know anywhere else to go.

PM   That's unjust! It had to be you. You were refreshment—my re-creation. You were what was best and dearest. What does a man turn to when he is in doubt, or despair, or even just horribly tired?

SARAH   To the Complex.

PM   What?

SARAH   To the Macadam Complex.

PM   I don't know what you're talking about.

SARAH   Oh, yes you do. Though you never called it by that
name, or recognized what it was. A man like you, Peter,
always has lots of women to look after him, and the
Macadam Complex is a very important group—nation-
ally important, for you are a national possession. There's
old Annie, who's been with us ever since we were
married, and who came to us from my mother's house;
she was supposed to be my comfort but in no time
at all she had surrendered completely to you. She's the
one who irons your shirts the way you like them, and
makes the kind of coffee you like, and sees that the
bedclothes at the foot of your bed are loosened every
night because you can't bear to have your feet confined.
And there's Miss Gobineau, who is so much more than
the perfect secretary, because she keeps you up to all
the latest idiom in Quebec French, never forgets an
appointment, never allows you to forget when somebody has done you a favour, knows where to lay her
hands on any one of five thousand important papers
whenever you want them, knows everything that is
said on the all-important Secretary Grapevine, and—
most important of all—knows how to keep her mouth
shut. And then, of course, there's me, and I know what
to do when you are in eclipse, or even in defeat, or
just hurt in your pride; I have the trick of understanding
things that have never been explained; I can manage
personal things that it wouldn't look well for you to do.
And I've mastered certain negative arts, as well. For
instance I never make friends who might want to get
at you through me; I know how to be respectable without being dull, and stylish without too often putting a
spanner in the works—which is harder than you'd
think. Annie: Miss Gobineau: myself—we are the Maca-

dam Complex, and without us there would be no Peter
Macadam as the world knows him.

SHAMAN   You have great power in your hand. Have you
never thought of throwing it up?

ARNAK   Every woman, at some time, has thought of throwing it up.

SARAH   But I'm not just every woman, you see.

ARNAK   Certainly not. And she owes that to you, doesn't
she, Hero?

PM   I have never thought so.

ARNAK   Oh yes you have; every man has thought so.

SARAH   You're too honest not to have thought so. But if I
were to throw it up, it would be very hard on you poli-
tically, wouldn't it, Peter? Why did she do it? Who's
the other woman? What nasty bed-tricks had he that
finally drove her out? Did she discover that he had a
boy-friend—

PM   They've never said that of me!

SARAH   Ask Miss Gobineau. Things that you never hear are
very carefully leaked to me, by people who pretend
they are being kind. But don't worry, my dear; I have
never thought seriously—not for more than a very few
minutes at a time—of leaving you. Even the best of
wives do, you know. But it wouldn't be fair to the
Complex, of which you are the sole capital and reason
for being. No, I've played fair, and if I haven't always
been loving, I've always been loyal.

PM   Loyalty! Is there no other reason for staying with me?

SARAH   But of course. Affection. Real affection. I don't say
love because I never know what people mean by it, and
we're to speak truth here, aren't we? But the truth is
that I'm not a fool: I know my destiny, and on the
whole it's a good one and I embrace it. I'm part of the
Macadam Complex. Not the greatest part, because that
is Peter Macadam himself. But I'm an indispensable

part. And many a one hath cast away her final worth when she hath cast away her servitude.

PM   My God! Where did you get that?

SARAH   At the Rideau Club. It was written in lipstick on the mirror in the Ladies' Room. It's what's called a *graffito*.

PM   But—servitude! Do you suppose I have no servitude to you?

SARAH   Your real servitude is to your work. I don't complain. But this is a place of truth. And so I say—servitude.

[*She goes.*]

PM   A place of truth! A place of destruction! Very well, if that is what it is to be, destroy me! You talk of decision to live or die: let it be death, then, and let me be rid of you!

ARNAK   If that's the way you want it, Hero. Though I think you're being a bit pettish.

PM   You talk of truth and then you strike at me through what is dearest to me, and what I counted on as most secure in my life. Must truth always be brutal?

SHAMAN   The truths we heed most are brutal. We think all the good things about us are the laws of our lives.

PM   Fantasies you call yourselves, as if you were strands in the fabric of my being! You are enemies and tormentors!

ARNAK   Hero, I've been thinking—serving you as your intelligence, you know. If you're going to die, couldn't we work up some splendid last words that Angatkok could radio down to Ottawa?

PM   Such as: I die for my country. Don't be a fool.

ARNAK   What I had in mind was something Canadians would really understand, like: This should be worth a full column in the *New York Times*! That'd be really Canadian. Come on, Hero; you owe it to your party!

SHAMAN   No, no: not time to talk of last words yet. You're out of temper, Mr. Macadam. You want to die to make us sorry. And no wonder; these confrontations with unpleasant truths rasp a man sorely. But the choice must still be made, and it would be a pity for you to make it in anger. The choice must come from deeper down than anger goes. Down into your depths with you, Mr. Macadam! Find your answer there. Time is running short, and they're waiting for your answer down below.

PM   Yes, I can imagine it.

SHAMAN   No need to imagine anything. Look.

[*Once again we see the* MINISTER FOR EXTERNAL AFFAIRS *talking to his faceless adviser.*]

MINISTER   At least we know a little more now than we did five days ago. He's on a mountain, somewhere up there. He's alive, it appears, though that can't go on forever. He may still make it. A great leader. When have I ever denied it? But there's a good chance—I mean a possibility, which we must never lose sight of—that he won't return. And I want everything ready to go the minute that chance becomes a certainty. I'll talk to the nation. Prime time, and on a Sunday night, even if it means holding up news of his death a few hours. I want the draft of my speech and I want the form to be right: regret, a first-class tribute with at least one good quotation that's easy to remember, and then a gradual change to sober optimism. We must go forward with the example of Peter Macadam glowing before us like his gonfalon, snatched from the Arctic snows—remember that about the gonfalon. And who's going to carry the gonfalon? Me! And don't make it too subtle. Make it a matter of obvious choice. . . .

[*We now see the office of the* SECRETARY OF STATE; *she is talking into a telephone.*]

SECRETARY   The only real difference between the two plans

40

is that in Number One we have the body, and in Number Two we don't. But the thing I want you to give your personal attention is the flag. If we have the body, the coffin must be covered with a big flag. We always get them from the armed forces and *they expect to get that flag back.* Now the last few state funerals we've had bad slip-ups. Somebody with a big heart grabs the flag and gives it to the widow, or something like that. Then the Army bills the widow for it, and it's a very, very bad show. Now I am relying on you—and I hold you personally responsible—for getting that flag back to where it came from. That is the single most important job in the whole memorial plan. . . . Who pronounces the blessing? I don't give a damn.

[*We are back on the Mountain.*]

SHAMAN   You see how they are steeling themselves for the worst.

PM   These are the professionals. Their job is not to feel but to make sure the nation feels, and feels the right way.

SHAMAN   I admire your coolness.

PM   I'm not cool. I'm boiling hot. I've never liked my Deputy Prime Minister, you know.

SHAMAN   So you're not disposed to oblige him?

PM   How?

SHAMAN   By dying. The decision must be made, and soon.

PM   Can I do it my own way?

SHAMAN   How else can you do anything?

PM   Very well, then. We'll find an answer.

SHAMAN   How, if I may ask?

PM   How but by the way I've made every important decision of my public career? How but by the methods I've learned in twenty-five years of public life? How but by the means that have been devised and refined by the most subtle intellects of the past five hundred years? Not all

41

wisdom is to be found in your primitive world, Dr. Angatkok! You tell me to call upon my depths: how can you know where my depths lie? To what have I given whatever is deepest in me? You shall see, and you shall hear!

[*The* PRIME MINISTER *is wild with delight, like a man who has wandered far, and is on familiar ground at last.*]

END ACT I

ACT II

THE ASPECT OF THE MOUNTAIN *has changed, and those who are familiar with the House of Commons will recognize some hint of its Gothic atmosphere. (This sort of magic is easy for designers and lighting experts, and they are invited to give us a fantastic evocation of the Commons Chamber.) The music also links the Arctic Sound with something hinting at pomp and circumstance.*

As the act begins the MINISTER FOR EXTERNAL AFFAIRS, ARNAK, *and the* SECRETARY OF STATE *enter and take places on the Government side of the House (left side from the audience's point of view), and* TIM, MARGE, *and* SARAH *take places on the Opposition side. They are informal and chat with one another until cries ring through the theatre of "Order! Order for the Speaker!" and the Speaker's procession enters.*

The SPEAKER *is the* SHAMAN, *fantastically dressed in robes that parody those of the Speaker of the Commons; in particular he wears an immense fur tricorne. Before him walks the* SERGEANT-AT-ARMS *bearing a mace, but both man and mace are from the world of fantasy; so also are the* SPEAKER'S CLERKS *who follow him. The procession should be a grotesque elaboration of the reality, frightening in effect.*

As the SPEAKER *takes his chair and bows to the assembly the cries change to "Question Time; Question Time".*

SHAMAN   We shall dispense with prayers.

MINISTER   Isn't that very unusual?

SHAMAN   This is an unusual session.

SECRETARY   In what way? We haven't had notice of anything special.

SHAMAN   Unusual because there is only one question to be answered: is the Prime Minister to live or die?

MARGE   Then you can count me out. I don't believe in capital punishment.

SHAMAN   It has nothing to do with capital punishment. We are assembled to advise the Prime Minister about a personal matter. It is this: in the present state of his physical, spiritual, and emotional life, will he or will he not recover his consciousness and return to Ottawa to his duties?

MARGE   I don't get it.

TIM   Then why don't you pipe down till you do get it?

ARNAK   Good advice!

MARGE   Says *whom*?

ARNAK   Says me! That's whom!

MARGE   Well, you won't get me to advise anybody to die. I wouldn't feel right.

SHAMAN   If it comes to a vote, you must vote. We do not permit abstentions here.

MINISTER   What kind of rule is that?

SHAMAN   A rule of this House.

MINISTER   What? Where are the parliamentary rules? Where's our copy of Beauchesne?

SHAMAN   We know only the rules decreed by the Queen.

MINISTER   The Queen? What Queen?

SHAMAN   That is an improper question.

MINISTER   But I mean—is this a direct royal interference with Parliament?

SHAMAN   It is a royal decree: not an interference.

MINISTER   I don't understand it.

SHAMAN   It is not necessary that you should.

MINISTER   But what Parliament is this?

SHAMAN   It is the Parliament of the Terra Incognita. It is Question Time. And I have told you the question.

MINISTER   But with all proper deference, it is not for the Speaker to put questions before the House.

SHAMAN   But I am the only one who knows what the question is.

LEADER OF THE OPPOSITION   Wait a moment. I know what the question is, and I am here to put it to the Prime Minister and his Government.

[*The* LEADER OF THE OPPOSITION *and the* PRIME MINISTER *have both taken their seats. They are the same man,* PETER MACADAM, *played by the same actor. When he speaks, his place on the other side of the House is taken by a double, as like him as possible except that he has no face; he is, indeed, the figure the* PM *encountered on the Mountain in Act One.*

For convenience the two characters are referred to in the text as PM(1) *to mean the Prime Minister and* PM(2) *to refer to the Leader of the Opposition.*]

SHAMAN   The House recognizes the Leader of the Opposition.

PM(2)   I have something to add to the question as it has already been put: will the Prime Minister live or die? To decide, must we not know who the Prime Minister is?

MINISTER   Oh, come. Isn't that rather stupid?

PM(2)   Too clear, perhaps? Not sufficiently plumped up with convenient debating points?

MINISTER   I don't see what debate there can be. We are talking about the Prime Minister, and his importance to his country is surely plain to everybody. If his health demands a holiday, I am perfectly willing, unworthy as I am, to act in his stead until he feels better. But this talk of death is unnecessary and really absurd. As my honourable friend on the other side of the House has already said, none of us wants to be associated with what might be interpreted as a decision for death. It revolts whatever is finest, and, I think I may say, bravest and most humane, in all of us.

GOVERNMENT MEMBERS   Hear, hear.

45

SECRETARY   I rise to support what my honourable friend, the Minister for External Affairs, has already said—

SHAMAN   Excuse me, does that mean you are going to say the same thing in different words?

SECRETARY   It does.

SHAMAN   Then why do we need to hear you?

SECRETARY   Excuse me, Mr. Speaker, this is a parliamentary custom of age-old acceptance. Repetition of an argument is a recognized way of giving it weight.

SHAMAN   But it's a waste of time.

MINISTER   No, sir; permit me to differ. There are undoubtedly those on the other side of the House who will welcome the opportunity to hear any point made twice, or even three times.

TIM   You mean we're stupid?

MINISTER   Say rather that you must be given every opportunity for consideration.

TIM   I don't need time. I've got the point now. Does he stick around or does he snuff it? Simple.

SECRETARY   Not simple except to simple minds. Suppose he snuffs it? Who's to take his place? Not my honourable friend, the Minister for External Affairs. God forbid! I've said it often and I'll say it again: a good Number Two. But a leader? We'd be out at the next election. Have some sense. The Prime Minister has to live.

MARGE   But why, if he doesn't want to?

SECRETARY   Look, whose side are you on? A few minutes ago you didn't want anything to do with his death. Now you've changed your tune. Why, if he doesn't want to? For the party, that's why!

MARGE   Aw, come on! Aren't there any other parties?

SECRETARY   Yes, but look at them! Everybody talks as if a country could throw up half a dozen governments whenever it likes. Let me tell you, most countries are lucky if they can raise one government that can do its job with anything that looks like efficiency. No government is stronger than its leader. If he can get a good group around him—fine. But they will never be stronger than he is himself.

ARNAK   Hurrah! That's what we want to hear. A leader! Be honest: say a Hero! Every country wants a Hero!

TIM   Hey, wait a minute! What about democracy?

ARNAK   Democracy be damned! The Hero! The Hero!

[*Uproar. The* SHAMAN *raises his hand and his clerks cry "Order, Order". The Sergeant-at-Arms moves forward to gesture the members back into their places.*]

SECRETARY   I am sure my honourable friend and colleague would apologize for her remark if she knew what apology meant. But she is, as you see, a primitive, and knows no better than to say exactly what she means. Those of us who belong to the modern world know that Heroes belong to the past.

ARNAK   Why?

SECRETARY   Because the Hero is absolute for victory; he must maintain his chosen course and his opinions come ruin, come exile, come death. But not the democratic leader. He is—he must be—a party man. The Hero lives in terms of Tragedy. The democratic leader lives in a world of Comedy—high comedy, black comedy, cruel and bitter comedy, farce and downright buffoonery— but always Comedy. Is that good? I don't know. I am a woman and in politics I must show myself fact-bound to prove I'm the equal of any man. So I say that Heroes are out—

ARNAK   Shame!

SECRETARY   It's part of the price we pay for a communal, democratic life. A high price, but perhaps not too high, because Tragedy is not only the world of the Hero but the world of the slave. Every democratic realist knows that part of the cost of democracy is the gelding of the Hero.

47

ARNAK How can you say Peter is a figure of Comedy when his job means he stands so much alone?

SARAH Alone?

ARNAK Isn't every man who has what it takes to be a Hero terribly alone?

SARAH I don't blame you for what you've just said. I'm not even greatly astonished. After all, what are you? I suppose you sit over there as a representation of Peter Macadam's intelligence. I don't suppose you've been able to divorce his intelligence from his egotism, for they always went hand in hand. Well, my intelligent friend, what do you think I am?

ARNAK You're Hero's wife, and sometimes I've wondered how you got the job.

SARAH Then your memory is shorter than mine. I didn't marry a Prime Minister, and it certainly never occurred to me that I was marrying a Hero. I married Peter Macadam.

ARNAK Didn't you think he might change and grow?

SARAH I didn't think he would grow into another man.

ARNAK You thought you were doing him a favour.

SARAH Yes; and he thought he was doing me a favour. We were both right—and both wrong.

ARNAK We're deciding whether he should live or die. Do you want him back?

SARAH I want what he wants. Preferably what Peter Macadam wants, but failing him—well, then, what the Prime Minister wants. What I want is whatever is necessary to the Complex. I shall not cast away my servitude.

SECRETARY Your servitude is your tragedy?

SARAH No. My servitude is my final worth, and I shall not be so foolish as to cast it away.

TIM Now there's somebody that talks sense. That guy Macadam's a Picker.

MARGE A slave! That's what men want in women. A slave!

48

SECRETARY   Servitude isn't slavery. Do you think I don't know? Who's free? Do you think Peter Macadam's free?

[*The* PRIME MINISTER *rises to speak; he is now on the Government side of the House and the faceless figure is in the seat he formerly occupied with the Opposition. In this character he is accomplished, assured, and shrewdly political, in contrast to the intense manner of the* LEADER OF THE OPPOSITION.]

PM(1)   Mr. Speaker, I think I am the person best qualified to speak about the freedom of the Prime Minister, and to define who the Prime Minister is. As the Secretary of State has already said, a country must be ruled by a group and that group must have a leader. Upon that leader devolves the chief responsibility for initiating new movements for the betterment of the country as a whole, sometimes by bringing about the betterment of special sections of the population—

TIM   Like the rich!

CLERKS   Order. Order.

TIM   Don't you order me! I got a right to speak, haven't I?

SHAMAN   You must speak in a reasonable and courteous manner.

TIM   What good did that ever do?

CLERKS   Order. Order.

TIM   What's all this Order-Order crap?

MARGE   It means you're not supposed to give the House a lot of your lip.

TIM   You pipe down!

MARGE   Listen, I'm a Person, see? The Parliament of Canada agreed—oh, years ago—that women are Persons. This is the House of Commons. We're not in that goddam little split-level now, and when I have any advice to give I'll give it, see?

TIM   Listen, I know about parliamentary rules. We have 'em in the union meetings—

MARGE   Union-schmunion! One of these days I'll be in a union of outraged women, so you'd just better watch it, see?

TIM   Yebbut have some sense! Why do I hafta pipe down just because some old weirdo in a big hat doesn't like what I say?

CLERKS   Order. Order.

SHAMAN   The Honourable Member for the Workers must not refer to the Speaker as an old weirdo. Any further disorder and I shall ask the Sergeant-at-Arms to eject the offender.

SECRETARY   [*Sotto voce*]   Throw the bugger out!

CLERKS   Order. Order.

TIM   You throw me out and I'll protest! I'll march! I'll march in my thousands, round and round and round—

MARGE   Till your feet hurt. Then you'll go and belly-ache to the papers. Now shut up!

SHAMAN   If the Honourable Member will not keep order, I shall place him under the personal authority of the Opponent of Capital Punishment.

TIM   [*Stricken*]   Jeez!

PM(I)   I was pointing out before an interruption that demonstrated as clearly as anything could do the problem of governing a free country, and therefore a country of varied opinions, that the task of the Government is not only to initiate, but to balance the interests of all sections of the population—including the rich, whom nobody likes but who, like the poor, are always with us—in an attempt to produce relative harmony and a strong state. It assumes authority, also, for the relations of our country with the other states of the world, even when they do not see eye to eye with us, confident that there is no state which does not desire peace in our time, and which is not prepared to come to a conference table where differences may be resolved, and cooperation assured.

GOVERNMENT MEMBERS   Hear, hear!

PM(1)   What, then, is the task of this Government's leader—

ARNAK   The Hero!

PM(1)   The enthusiasm of a Government supporter erupts in a cry of "Hero". No, Mr. Speaker, not a Hero, but one who because of his unusual—may I say unique—capacity to apprehend and to weigh the tasks of government becomes for that reason its humblest, most devoted and most concerned servant. He throws whatever he may have of physical endurance—

ARNAK   Attaboy, Hero!

PM(1)   —of ratiocinative faculty, amounting, when he is capable of it, to wisdom—

[*Cheer from Government supporters.*]

—of his adroitness as a persuader and debater—

ARNAK   [*Sotto voce*]   That's me!

PM(1)   —to the public service. And what reward does he ask? Is there any reward in the gift of a democratic state commensurate with the demands it makes on its leader? A title? What prouder title does Canada offer than the one he already bears—the title that expresses his servitude? Wealth? What riches lie in his grasp that an honest man may take, which requite him for health and energies strained to the uttermost? No, his reward is his vision of this young and vigorous country as it may be, his faith in its destiny, its people, and its future!

[*Sensation among the Government supporters; the MINISTER FOR EXTERNAL AFFAIRS hastens to shake the PM's hand, as does the SECRETARY OF STATE. ARNAK is beside herself, jumps up and down in her place, and when she can get at the PM kisses him rapturously. But the OPPOSITION is silent and dubious. In the confusion the PM joins the OPPOSITION as PM(2) and the double returns to his seat in the Government.*]

PM(2)   I hear nothing in all this that tells me who the Prime

Minister is. His colleagues know him only as a political functionary. When I heard him speak, it seemed to me that I heard the office rather than the man. Is he no more than an appendage of a country? Very well, I introduce a supplementary question: what sort of country are we talking about? It seems to be perpetually in a state of *becoming*. We are never told what it *is*. We know what other countries are. We know what Britain is. We know with growing disquiet what the United States is. When we sit at one of those conference tables the Prime Minister spoke of with such unction, we know what countries our colleagues represent. Because we know the countries, to some extent we know the man. But what are we?

MINISTER Mr. Speaker, if I understand the Leader of the Opposition aright, it is his intention to divert this House to a discussion of what is fashionably called the Identity Crisis. The solution of that problem may be left safely—or if not safely, at least with relief and gratitude—to the Canada Council.

PM(2) My question was put to the Prime Minister. Has he no answer? What kind of country?

SHAMAN Will the House please address itself to the supplementary question: What kind of country is Canada?

SECRETARY I don't understand the question.

PM(2) Is it a country which acts upon the world, or is it acted upon by the world? More simply, is it a country that happens to the world, or does the world happen to it? Is it an extraverted or an introverted country?

SECRETARY Mr. Speaker, these are metaphysical questions. They have no place here. We deal in practicalities.

SHAMAN In this House metaphysical matters are pressing matters. I refer you to the supplementary question.

PM(2) Who loves this country?

MINISTER Love! Love! Love! Is it necessary for the modern economic unit—I mean the free citizen—to love his land like some peasant of the long-ago?

PM(2)   If he doesn't love it he must understand it, and if he can't understand it he must at least be jealous of it, or in this greedy, hungry world he must lose it. Who is in the Arctic now? Who navigates our Northwest Passage —beneath its surface? What was the first thing I encountered when I came here? Look! Look!

[*The* TWO EXPLORERS *whom we saw at the beginning of the play are propelled onto the stage by the Sergeant-at-Arms; the* FIRST *is in terror, the* SECOND *defiant.*]

FIRST EXPLORER   We have taken nothing.

SECOND EXPLORER   Nothing but a few rock samples.

FIRST EXPLORER   For comparison only.

PM(2)   What are you doing here?

SECOND EXPLORER   Science knows no national boundaries. Our interest is scientific and international.

PM(2)   What are you doing here?

FIRST EXPLORER   We shall regularize our position at the first opportunity.

SECOND EXPLORER   Or it will be regularized for us.

FIRST EXPLORER   Perhaps that has been done already.

PM(2)   What are you doing here?

FIRST EXPLORER   We are trying to find out what you have.

SECOND EXPLORER   We are searching for what you are too idle, and too unadventurous, to take.

[*They go, as swiftly as they came.*]

PM(2)   You see. If we do not love the land for what it is, there are others who love it in a very different way for what it has. Now tell me—who loves this country?

MINISTER   Love of country may be taken for granted. But you must not press a twentieth-century people to make a public parade of patriotism.

PM(2)   So they love in secret?

MINISTER   If you wish to put it that way.

53

PM(2)   What do they love?

MINISTER   Well, many things. For instance, their heritage.

PM(2)   May we call that heritage?

[*The* SHAMAN *nods, but the* HERITAGE *has already appeared. He is a very old* HERALD, *silvery, courteous, and charming, dressed in the full panoply of his office—silken breeches and stockings, a cocked hat, and a resplendent tabard; he carries the ornate baton proper to his office. But there is about him a general shabbiness, and dustiness, and perhaps even a cobweb or two. He bows with grave courtesy to the* SPEAKER, *and then to the House.*]

PM(2)   Let us hear our heritage.

HERALD   Symbolically represented. I have, as you see, the Lion and Unicorn, the Lions of Scotland, the Irish Harp, the Lilies of France, the Lilies of Brabant, the Lions of Orange-Nassau, and a fine menagerie of double-headed eagles, hippogryphs, golden suns, and all the wonders of the ancient world, to signify Poland, and Russia, and Italy, and Portugal and—dear me, so many lands that have contributed to this one that I am sure to leave somebody out if I try to name them all. Even my stockings, you observe, are silk, which is a compliment to our large Chinese community. My underclothing is of that healthy variety that comes from the Scandinavian lands. I am as symbolic as it lies in my power to be.

TIM   Yeah, but what the hell do you do?

HERALD   I am a Herald. These are, I assure you, my working clothes.

TIM   But what can you do in that outfit?

HERALD   I am a Remembrancer. I remind you of what you were, so that you may have a clearer idea of what you are, and can therefore decide intelligently what you may become. I am the continuance of history.

TIM   By gollies you haven't got anything to do with me! Nope, I'm through with all that. Look at you! All silk and feathers and fancy crap—continuance of history! Not my history.

HERALD Are you sure? What is your history?

TIM My history is made up of all the people who came here with nothing—not a cent—and made their own way.

PM(2) All honour to them. But only unhappy people emigrate. Where did they come from?

TIM What do you mean, unhappy? Are you calling me unhappy?

PM(2) What happiness do I see in your face, fellow-citizen?

TIM I'll have all the happiness I need when there's been a few changes made. Not before. And what's it matter where my gang came from?

HERALD Well, it's history; that's why it matters. There are no new beginnings.

TIM Okay then. They musta come from someplace. But they came to get away from you, and all that fancy junk.

HERALD Fancy junk?

TIM The romantic stuff.

HERALD Oh, my friend, there is no romance so potent as the belief that one can get rid of one's past. So do not, I beg you most sincerely, do not reject the fancy junk, as you call it. If I were to show you the unadorned reality of your past, it would sadden you, and perhaps it might break you. Who are you? I don't know. Were you one of the Scots who were shipped to Canada like cattle because their own chieftains had betrayed them for English money? Were you one of the Irish who came because a gentleman-gambler recouped his fortunes by sending his peasants to Canada, at the price of a pound a head? From what more recent abyss of misery and betrayal do you spring? But you had a past: that is as certain as that you have a present. So I beg you to accept me, absurd as I must sometimes appear, for I am a nourishing, romantic legend.

TIM You think I can't stand the truth?

55

PM(2)   Why should you demand only the ugliest part of the truth? This also is part of the truth.

TIM   He don't look like truth to me. He looks like he's on the side of the bigshots.

PM(2)   Well, dismaying though you may find it, the bigshots make history because they have the energy and the ruthlessness and the desire to do so, and there is nothing that you or I can do about it. If you want the unadorned truth, I will strip our Heritage of what you call his fancy junk, and all you will see is a naked old creature, humbled by the loss of his dreams. Not even philosophers can endure that: nations need dreams, and not only dreams of the future.

MINISTER   If I may intervene, I think what our friend here means is that there is nothing about this Heritage that speaks directly of the country we know. And I entirely agree. Surely our symbolism must be home-grown. Let us, in everything, be ourselves. Away, I say, with borrowings. Though I myself can only claim to be a practical politician, in no sense a man of unusual abilities—

[*He pauses for contradiction, but there is none, and he is rather disconcerted.*]

—I am always conscious, when I take my place in the House of Commons, of the great figures who have sat there before me, and from whose shades—if you will permit a flight of fancy—I seem to draw sustenance. Among them, surely, there must be some who give us the heroic inspiration we seek. Indeed, I am convinced of it. If we could but see them—

TIM   Naw! I don't want to see any more guys with feathers in their hats.

PM(2)   This is always the difficulty with national heroes. They ought to be enthroned in the hearts of their people, but what can you do for a people in whose hearts there are no thrones?

56

TIM There, you see! Thrones! Haven't you got anything to offer but this feather-and-throne crap?

HERALD Oh, certainly. I am infinitely accommodating. Many countries do very well with a totem-figure, often an animal—

PM(2) Wait! Wait! I beg you to be careful with animals—

SHAMAN So you *are* capable of learning something new, Mr. Macadam? Well done, man, well done!

PM(2) Better to let the animal choose you!

MINISTER But it has! Why didn't I think of that before? The Beaver!

HERALD Oh, my dear fellow, I entreat you—not the Beaver.

MINISTER What's wrong with the Beaver?

HERALD Will it suffice if I say that no country can hope to rise above mediocrity if it lacks a mystique of the courage, the humour, and also the cunning and roguery of its people—

MINISTER Exactly, and I repeat—what's wrong with the Beaver?

[*The* BEAVER *has joined them; he is a sleek and in every respect admirable fellow, whose white shirt, highly polished shoes, neat blue serge suit of conservative cut, and beautifully brushed hair seem wholly in his favour. He has, unfortunately, rather prominent upper front teeth and almost no forehead, but his smile speaks of unlimited self-satisfaction. If his figure has a fault, it is a heaviness about the hips and a shortness of leg, and when he speaks, he occasionally emphasizes a point by smacking his hands together with a damp Splat! that suggests some large flat object striking water.*]

BEAVER Nothing whatever wrong with the Beaver, I can assure you. Busy, busy, busy. But never too busy to be of help. Now—how can I be of assistance?

MINISTER We were speaking of you as a national symbol.

SECRETARY Something that unites. Something everybody agrees to love and respect.

ARNAK A totem animal for an old country with new people.

BEAVER Well—well, I don't like to push myself forward. But I have been spoken of in that way. It would be false modesty to deny it.

TIM I don't know that I like this fellow, either. He's got a managerial look about him.

BEAVER No, no, no. I can roll up my sleeves, but only after I've thought and planned. Make haste slowly—but not too slowly, eh? Keep everlastingly at it, eh? Stick-to-itiveness is what wins, eh?

TIM What did I tell ya? A stakhanovite! Naw! You won't do. Give me the Maple Leaf any day.

BEAVER All right, I can give you the Maple Leaf any day, any hour, almost any minute. Crrrunch! Crunch-crunch-crunch-crunch! Timber! Wham! And I've laid it at your feet. Your Maple Leaf is a johnny-come-lately compared with me. If it hadn't been for jealousy in high places I'd be on the flag. Industry. That's how we build a modern nation.

MINISTER I certainly can't find fault with that.

TIM Naw! Only on the condition that industry ensures a paradise for the worker.

BEAVER Certainly! A big beaver lodge with everybody snug and dry inside it—after the day's work is done. I like you. I particularly like the way you keep saying Gnaw! That's how we'll build the Worker's Paradise: gnaw, gnaw, gnaw.

MARGE You got him wrong. He's a great union man. He doesn't say Gnaw. He just says Naw.

BEAVER No problem. A little remedial work on his front teeth will fix that. Then you'll hear him say Gnaw.

TIM The hell you will!

BEAVER Oh yes. Remember that there was at least one great civilization in this country before any of you arrived.

It was the beaver's civilization. Fraternally organized. Lodges everywhere. Lumbering on an extraordinary scale. Everybody happy. Happy, happy beavers. Now I'm sure this gentleman in the fancy pinafore has been telling you about the advantages of giving proper heed to your past. You might very well give a thought to that beaver civilization. We had no problems.

TIM   Commie bastards!

BEAVER   Co-operative, certainly; not bastards. Industry and morality went hand in hand. We mated monogamously and we coddled our kits—

MINISTER   Of course our national interests have expanded since that idyllic time. We now have to work with other nations—

BEAVER   Ah, yes; but we have a formula for that. The Honest Broker, eh?

MINISTER   That's what we've been called, certainly. The Honest Broker. A proud name.

BEAVER   And you've done it according to the Beaver Formula.

MINISTER   I've never heard that.

BEAVER   Oh, yes.

HERALD   Oh, wretched animal! I knew this would happen!

BEAVER   What's the matter with you?

HERALD   You and your Beaver Formula. You are invited to appear as a national totem, and you talk of your disgraceful Formula!

BEAVER   It's always worked, hasn't it?

HERALD   But at what a cost! Honour sacrificed! More than honour!

SHAMAN   What formula is under discussion?

HERALD   I ask your pardon, Mr. Speaker. But the Beaver Formula robs me of all sense of propriety.

PM(2)   Will you define it for us?

BEAVER   Surely I should do that?

SHAMAN   The Herald has the ear of the House.

59

HERALD   How am I to phrase it? I speak, you know, for the wisdom of the past. Sometimes my office, and my attitude toward life, is spoken of as medieval. I don't mind. There was great wisdom in the Middle Ages. The people in those times were very strong on symbols, and to every animal they attributed a symbolic significance. Thus, the Pelican, which fed its young with its own blood, stood for piety; the Ox stood for patience; but the Beaver stood for a certain sort of diplomacy. Must I go on?

SHAMAN   Is it the will of the House?

EVERYBODY   Aye! Aye!

HERALD   As you wish, then. The Beaver's industry and good-will were conceded by everyone. [BEAVER: Thank you, thank you.] Arguing somebody else's cause the Beaver was eloquent and fair. [BEAVER: Very kind of you.] But if, in an argument with any greater animal—be it the Lion, the Eagle, the Bear, or what you will—the greater animal spoke to the Beaver in a sufficiently loud and hectoring tone, the Beaver would make a peace-offering to his opponent by biting off and offering—his own testicles. [BEAVER: But—but—but—] This made the Beaver the mockery of the animal kingdom; quite small animals with loud voices would leap out from hiding and shout "Boo!" just to see the Beaver roll over and put into effect its policy of appeasement.

[*The* BEAVER *is whistling feebly.*]

You see, it never developed a good voice. The Lion offered to teach it to roar; the Eagle proposed a short course in screaming; even the Hyena suggested that it might learn to laugh. But the Beaver was true to its own nature, and never produced any sound greater than a short whistle. Now I put it to you, Mr. Speaker, with all the emphasis that inheres in my traditional office, is this the kind of diplomacy you wish to embrace? Is this the example you wish to present to a nation? Is this the creature you would exalt to the dignity of a national totem?

[*Pause while they think.* BEAVER *whistles intermittently.*]

SECRETARY You have to watch your step with the big fellows.

MINISTER Appeasement, allied to goodwill and intelligence, is not an ineffective policy.

HERALD No, gentlemen, no! The sacrifice the Beaver makes for what it calls peaceful co-existence is irreversible. It is a simple fact of sovereignty: when the orbs are gone, the sceptre is unavailing! No!

SARAH And I say no!

MARGE Me too!

EVERYONE No! No!

[*Uproar*]

CLERKS Order! Order!

SHAMAN The decision seems to be against you.

EVERYBODY Out! Out! Out!

CLERKS Order! Order!

[*The cries of "No! No!" mount and the* BEAVER *loses his composure completely. In desperation he produces a large pair of scissors and offers them to his opponents; his whistles are pitiful. The* SHAMAN *rises and everyone who is not already standing rises with him.*]

SHAMAN Take away that Beaver!

[*The* SERGEANT-AT-ARMS, *with drawn sword, approaches the* BEAVER, *who collapses utterly, falling on his back in an obliging position. With the help of the* CLERKS *he is dragged from the scene, uttering plaintive whistles.*]

MINISTER I'm sorry about that. But how was I to know? He seemed such a nice fellow.

SECRETARY But an extremist.

TIM Jeez, what some people will do to get their faces on a stamp!

MINISTER   How did he get as far he did?

PM(2)   Because people like you want a pet, not a totem. If anyone can pet your totem or order it to kennel you may be sure they'll do the same to you.

SHAMAN   [*In an undertone*] Yes, you do learn, Mr. Macadam, and there's hope for you yet.

[*The* SERGEANT-AT-ARMS *and the* CLERKS *return; the* SHAMAN *sits. He nods to the* PM(2).]

PM(2)   Am I to go on?

SHAMAN   Return to the question, if you please.

PM(2)   I asked the Prime Minister who he was, and he gave me an unsatisfactory answer. I asked what sort of country this was and the answer was no better. Let me ask a third question: Why does anybody want to be Prime Minister?

[*Laughter, boos, and catcalls from* ARNAK, *the* MINISTER FOR EXTERNAL AFFAIRS, *and the* SECRETARY OF STATE. *In the mêlée the* PM *changes to the* GOVERNMENT *side, his double to the* OPPOSITION.]

PM(1)   Mr. Speaker, surely we have some rule for suppressing purely frivolous questions?

SARAH   Please—not a frivolous question. A question that has puzzled me during many a troubled hour. So allow me to repeat it: Why does anybody want to be Prime Minister?

PM(1)   Mr. Speaker, the question is not so much frivolous as naive.

[*This time the protest and angry laughter is from the* OPPOSITION.]

SARAH   Naive, Peter? You say that to me? Naive?

MINISTER   Mr. Speaker, my colleague is under some embarrassment because of the source of the question. May I speak on his behalf? The protests of the Opposition make it clear they expect candour. Very well. The

Prime Minister is a statesman and has spoken like a statesman. Let me speak simply as a party man. Because —we must be realistic—behind the statesman stands a party. Now, what is a party? It is a faction: not a mean faction or a narrowly based faction, not a plot against the public weal. But none the less a faction that seeks —as you see, I am utterly frank—to have its own way. Give a party its own way, and it may rule very well.

TIM   He admits it! You hear him, everybody? He admits it. Stamp on everybody; get the best of everybody; have your own way. What'd happen if a union behaved like that? What about the rest of us? What about me?

MINISTER   Well, my friend, what about you? We're both in the same boat. As things stand your job is rowing ·and mine is steering, and I'm steering for you just as much —and rather more—than you're rowing for me. If you think you're a steersman, get the job. It's always up for grabs.

TIM   Easy to say, for the higher-ups! What about real equality?

MINISTER   The only equality we have is our common human- ity. That's poor comfort, but it's a fact, and I didn't make it one.

ARNAK   And the Hero? What about the Hero?

SARAH   You're all wrong; quite wrong. When I ask why any man wants to be Prime Minister, I ask why he wants to pay the terrible price of high office—

PM(I)   I suppose you mean, why does any man want a job that takes him away from domestic concerns.

SARAH   That was unkindly said. No: why does any man want a job that estranges him from himself?

PM(I)   Mr. Speaker, is the debate to proceed on this very personal level?

SARAH   Oh, you fool! — Oh my dear, my very dear! We are debating whether you will live or die, and you are determined to argue against yourself. The personal level!

Are you so stupid, so besotted with public concerns, that you don't know that everything—everything in the world—comes at last from what you call the personal level? The Prime Minister cannot rise above the level of Peter Macadam, and the party cannot rise above the level of the Prime Minister. What is a man that other men should exalt him if he is not someone whose life on the personal level—on the deepest bedrock of the personal level—is of worth, and colour and substance and splendour that makes him a man in whom other men see something of what is best in themselves?

MINISTER I sympathize. Please understand me: I sympathize profoundly. But surely you realize how far this lies from the realities of public life?

SARAH So much the worse for public life!

SECRETARY But you must understand that by and large people in public life are sincere. They really do speak and act from the best that's in them.

MARGE I guess that's what makes it so pathetic.

TIM If that's their best, God spare us from their worst!

SARAH But it isn't their best! The best is lost and trampled in the scramble.

PM(I) Oh, come on, Sarah! You're not going to bring out that tired old crack about power corrupting and absolute power corrupting absolutely?

SARAH No. I wasn't going to say that. I don't believe power corrupts. I believe it is losing touch with the source of power that corrupts.

PM(I) The source of power? You're talking very big, my dear. What source of power are you talking about?

SARAH Whom do you serve?

PM(I) My country.

SARAH I didn't say what: I said whom.

PM(I) My people, then.

SARAH All of them?

PM(1)   That would be claiming too much.

SARAH   Do you serve Peter Macadam?

[*Protests from* GOVERNMENT *and* OPPOSITION.]

PM(1)   You, of all people, ought to know that his own concerns are the last considerations that should influence a Prime Minister.

SARAH   A mad answer! A lunatic answer! You describe a man without a core! An empty man! And that is my sorrow for you! You represent millions, and you have lost your hold on the one man who is all you have and all you can ever know of life.

PM(1)   I must keep my face to the world.

SARAH   Then you will see nothing but the world.

PM(1)   The world has served me very well.

SARAH   So well that we are debating whether you shall live or die, and you have no opinion to offer. Poor Peter! Oh, my poor, poor Peter!

PM(1)   You cannot break me with your pity or your tears. You knew me when you linked yourself with me— when you joined what you now like to call the Macadam Complex. I was ambitious: yes. I wanted to cut some figure in history: yes. I wanted power: yes. And have you ever known a man who was worth a second look who did not, in one way or another, want all these things? And if I die now, shall I not have had them all?

SARAH   The statesman and the Prime Minister will not die. He is already safe in history. But what about Peter Macadam? Must Peter die without ever having had his say?

PM(1)   Surely we need not waste time on this quibble, Mr. Speaker?

SHAMAN   Not a quibble, but a truth you will not face. Your wife has spoken well: the public man is secure in the public memory. But it is the private man who must die,

65

and what sort of death will it be if the private man has never truly lived?

PM(1) Who cares about the quality of a death?

HERALD Anyone, surely, who has advanced beyond the elementary wisdom of caring about the quality of a birth?

PM(1) Don't suppose I am ungrateful for the Macadam Complex. But you were wrong to say I was the property of the Complex. I am nobody's property. I have always stood alone, and gloried in standing alone.

ARNAK [In a whisper] At last you've admitted it! The Hero! Yes, it is—the Hero!

PM(1) I have given the best that is in me to the world that lies about me. You think that not enough. You ask for more. And what is it you want? Do you think I don't know? It is nothing more than the desire—the demand —of every woman for admission that she has been more to her man than all the world, its demands, duties, and triumphs. That's what women really mean when they talk of the inner life, and attainment of selfhood, and all that romantic twaddle. Am I to agree to that lie? I am amazed you should ask it of me.

SARAH I am desolated that your egotism is so great that you can see nothing but a lesser egotism in me. Can you truly think I am clinging to a stupid woman's proprietorship?

PM(1) Then for what in me do you plead?

SARAH I can't command it in words, but I know it's the truth. If I could say—if I were sure—

SHAMAN Let those speak for you who can.

HERALD Most certainly you speak of the Queen.

PM(1) Who gives you permission to speak unasked?

HERALD Natural authority. Great age and experience. And I am a servant of the Queen. As we all are, whether we know it or not.

PM(1) Your Queen has no real power here. She is a legal convenience and a romantic ideal—

66

HERALD Excuse me; I don't think you understand. The Queen we serve here is no fiction; she is as real as the air we breathe: she is the final reality: she is ourselves, our forebears, and our children; she is this land—so old it makes all monarchies seem like passing shadows on her face, and all forms of power like games children tire of. She is the Queen to whom all earthly queens are shadowy vice-gerents.

PM(I) I will hear no more! I asked for this House to sit because I thought it would be the place where I am most used to answering questions. A place where truth or working compromise can be discovered by rational means. But what do I find? I am betrayed. The Speaker permits what should not be permitted: people speak who have no mandate to speak: twisting questions are asked that are outside any power of decision. I ask for reason and you give me a Parliament of Irrationality!

SHAMAN What do you expect when you are wandering in Les Montagnes de Glace, Mr. Macadam? Do you suppose that your House of what you call realities in Ottawa is the only House in which you hold office? No, no: our Parliament of Irrationalities is the great governing body of all the earth, where every man is his own Prime Minister, holding office under the Queen. It is here that we truly rule and decide. So if you hope to be strong in that other House you must give faithful duty in this one. Let me tell you that defeat here—final defeat—is worse than any rejection there. Defeat here is loss of yourself. That is why I have allowed you to be pressed so hard, and questioned so shrewdly.

PM(I) I will answer no more. I demand a dissolution.

SHAMAN Only the Queen can dissolve this House, Mr. Macadam. Do you ask for an audience with her?

PM(I) Yes! Yes; anything but this.

[*The* SHAMAN *rises and all rise.*]

HERALD The Queen!

67

[*She enters, the* HERALD *walking backward before her; her entry is accompanied by the Arctic Sound. There is nothing about her now of the pathos of Act One. She gestures toward the mace, which the* SERGEANT-AT-ARMS *lifts from its place; as he does so all the characters bow or curtsy, and leave the stage slowly and in silence. Only the* PRIME MINISTER, *and* PM(2), *and the* SHAMAN *remain.*]

TIM I know her! I've known her since—since—you know her, don't you?

MARGE Yeah, But I didn't know you were like that.

TIM Well, I am.

[*They go. In the scene that follows, the emphasis is contrary to that of the scene in Act One in which the* PM *spoke with the echo, for here it is he who is the echo, and* LA SORCIERE *the positive voice. Both figures, the* PM *and the double, approach her, and at first the answers are stubborn and defiant.*]

LA SORCIERE Peter Macadam.

PM(I) Madam?

LA SORCIERE The time has come when you must answer, Peter.

PM(I) Answer Peter.

LA SORCIERE You invite me to answer you? Then you are wiser than I have thought.

PM(I) I have thought.

LA SORCIERE Indeed you have thought. You think so brilliantly, so incisively, so enviably. But how enviably do you feel?

PM(I) Feel?

LA SORCIERE Feeling is hard for you. You have taken an easy way, and sought your godhead in thought, which comes so smoothly ... so delusively. It has made you very proud.

PM(I) Very proud.

68

LA SORCEIRE   Very proud. But not very understanding, or very compassionate, or very aware. Not always very good.

PM(1)   Always very good.

LA SORCIERE   You answer mockingly. That is not the spirit I ask from you. Not the spirit in which I speak to you. You are stubborn and proud of it.

PM(1)   Proud of it.

LA SORCIERE   Brilliant, enviable, stubborn man, how do you answer your great question: Will you live or die?

PM(1)   Live—or die.

LA SORCIERE   Then you do not care?

PM(1)   Do not care.

LA SORCIERE   Do you hope to deceive me with a heartless stoicism? Do you think I do not know it for what it is: want of understanding for yourself; want of knowledge of yourself; want of compassion for yourself. Posturing as a strong man; posturing as one who loves, who leads, who serves a whole people, but without any true, humble love for the creature he should cherish most? Child, child!

[*The* PM's *defiance has been on the wane, and now it is as* PM(2) *that he speaks, and the double begins to fade before our eyes.*]

PM(2)   Child?

LA SORCIERE   Child—and lover.

PM(2)   Lover?

LA SORCIERE   Have you not lived long enough in my country to be both child and lover to what I am? And how you have used me! Wilful, stubborn, resolute in seeking another way—any pitiful, shallow, frivolous way—when you could find all things if you would turn to me.

PM(2)   Turn to me!

LA SORCIERE   It is not I who have turned away. I have always been near. Fool! Child! Fool-child! You have made me bring you here, strike you down from the sky to this

69

moment of the great question, because nothing else would make you turn your face to me.

PM(2)   Turn your face to me!

LA SORCIERE   I do; I do, my child, my lover. Never turn your face from me again.

PM(2)   Oh goddess!—Never turn your face from me again!

LA SORCIERE   Never, Peter? Then your question is answered.

PM(2)   Answered!

SHAMAN   Answered!

[*The* PM *falls to his knees and puts his hands in hers in an act of homage and submission. Immediately we are whisked back into the gaudily coloured world of the* TV HEAD, *who appears on his screen.*]

TV HEAD   The Prime Minister, the Right Honourable Peter Macadam, has been found alive and well, though somewhat weakened by his ordeal, in the farthest Arctic, in the region of Les Montagnes de Glace. A search plane that has been hovering in the area just outside the storm that has enclosed the Mountains for several days is already on its way to rescue the Prime Minister and carry him to a larger plane that will bring him back to the capital. That's the news. Lloyd Robertson for The National.

[*On the Mountain again, we see a* PILOT *extending his hand to the* PRIME MINISTER, *who shakes it.*]

PILOT   Gee, I certainly am glad to see you! We've got to get out of here fast. The storm may close in again any time. Terrible place for weather, this is. I hate to say it, but it's lucky you're alone. I mean I wouldn't want to take more than one. Got anything to take out with you?

PM(2)   More than I brought.

PILOT   Eh? Nothing too heavy, I hope?

PM(2)   No, no; I was joking. Only myself.

PILOT   Oh. That'll be enough though, eh?

[*They go, and not far off we hear the waiting plane revving up its engine. With a roar it is off, and as its shadow passes overhead the* SHAMAN *lifts his hand in farewell. He turns to the throne, but* LA SORCIERE *has gone. He makes his own way slowly over the Mountain waste as the Arctic Sound is heard in its last form, and the Mountain loses all colour but that of ice.*]

E N D